Course	Anatomy & Physiology I/II
Course Number	**BIO 230/260**
	California Univ Of Pa
	BIOLOGICAL SCIENCE

http://create.mheducation.com

ISBN-10: 1121387128   ISBN-13: 9781121387126

Contents

Credits

Student Preface

This laboratory manual was written to help you gain experience in the lab as you learn human anatomy and physiology. The 47 exercises explore and explain the structure and function of the human body. You will be asked to study the structure of the body using the materials available in your lab, which may consist of models, charts, mammal study specimens such as cats, preserved or fresh internal organs of sheep or cows, and possibly cadaver specimens. You may also examine microscopic sections from various organs of the body. You should familiarize yourself with the microscopes in your lab very early, so that you can take the best advantage of the information they can provide.

The physiology portion of the course involves experiments that you will perform on yourself or your lab partner. They may also involve the mixing of various chemicals and the study of the functions of live specimens. Because the use of animals in experiments is of concern to many students, a significant attempt has been made to reduce (but, unfortunately, not eliminate) the number of live experiments in this manual. Until there is a sound replacement for live animals, their use will continue to be part of the college physiology lab. Your instructor may have alternatives to live animal experimentation exercises. It is important to get the most out of what live specimen experimentation there is. Coming to the lab unprepared and then sacrificing a lab animal while gaining little or no information is an unacceptable waste of life. Use the animals with care. Needless use or inhumane treatment of lab animals is not acceptable or tolerated.

As a student of anatomy and physiology you will be exposed to new and detailed information. The time it takes to learn the information will involve *more* than just time spent in the lab. You should maximize your time in the lab by reading the assigned lab exercises before you come to class. You will be doing complex experiments, and if you are not familiar with the procedure, equipment, and time involved you could ruin the experiment for yourself and/or your lab group. The

exercises in physiology are written so you can fill in the data as you proceed with the experiment. At the end of each exercise are review sheets that your instructor may wish to collect to evaluate the data and conclusions of your experiments. The illustrations are labeled except on the review pages. All review materials can be used as study guides for lab exams or they may be handed in to the instructor.

The anatomy exercises are written for cat and human study, though these exercises can be used with or without cats or cadavers. Get *involved* in your lab experience. Don't let your lab partner do all the dissections or all the experimentation; likewise, don't insist on doing everything yourself. Share the responsibility and you will learn more.

Safety

Safety guidelines appear in the inside front cover for reference. The international symbol for caution (⚠) is used throughout the manual to identify material that you should pay close and special attention to when preparing for or performing laboratory exercises.

Clean Up

Special instructions are provided for clean up at the end of appropriate laboratory exercises and are identified by this unique icon (🧽).

How to Study for This Course

Some people learn best by concentrating on the visual, some by repeating what they have learned, and others by writing what they know over and over again. In this course, you will have to adapt your learning style to different study methods. You may use one study method to learn the muscles of the body and a completely different method for understanding the function of the nervous system. Some students need only a few hours per week to succeed in this course, while others seem to study far longer.

You need to go to class. Go to lab on time. The beginning of the lab is when most instructors go over the material and point out what material to omit, what to change, and how to proceed. If you do not attend lab, you do not get the necessary information.

Read the material ahead of time. The subject matter is visual, and you will find an abundance of illustrations in this manual. Record on your calendar all the lab quizzes and exams listed on the syllabus provided by your instructor. Budget your time so you study accordingly.

Work hard! There is absolutely no substitute for hard work to achieve success in a class. Some people do math more easily than others, some people remember things more easily, and some people express themselves better. Most students succeed because they work hard at learning the material. It is a rare student who gets a bad grade because of a lack of intelligence. Working at your studies will get you much farther than worrying about your studies.

Be *actively* involved with the material and you will learn it better. Outline the material after you study it for a while. Read your notes, go over the material in your mind, and then make the information your own. There are several ways that you can get actively involved.

Draw and doodle a lot. Anatomy is a visual science, and drawing helps. You do not have to be a great illustrator. Visualize the material in the same way you would draw a map to your house for a friend. You do not draw every bush and tree but, rather, create a *schematic* illustration that your friend could use to get the *pertinent* information. As you know, there are differences in maps. Some people need more practice than others, but anyone can do it. The head can be a circle, which can be divided into pieces representing the bones of the skull. Draw and label the illustration after you have studied the material and without the use of your text! Check yourself against the text to see if you really know the material. Correct the illustration with a colored pen, so that you highlight the areas you need work on. Go back and do it again until you get it perfect. This does take some time, but not as much as you might think.

Write an outline of the material. Take the mass of information to be learned and go from the general to the specific. Let's use the skeletal system as an example. You may wish to use these categories:

1. Bone composition and general structure
2. Bone formation
3. Parts of the skeleton
   a. Appendicular skeleton
      (1) Pectoral girdle
      (2) Upper extremity
      (3) Pelvic girdle
      (4) Lower extremity
   b. Axial skeleton
      (1) Skull
      (2) Hyoid
      (3) Ribs
      (4) Vertebral column
      (5) Sternum

An outline helps you organize the material in your mind and lets you sort the information into areas of focus. If you do not have an organizational system, then this course is a jumble of terms with no interrelationships. The outline can get more detailed as you progress, so you eventually know that the specific nasal bone is one of the facial bones and the facial bones are skull bones, which are part of the axial skeleton, which belongs to the skeletal system.

Test yourself before the exam or quiz. If you have practiced answering questions about the material you have studied, then you should do better on the real exam. As you go over the material, jot down possible questions to be answered later, after you study. If you compile a list of questions as you review your notes, then you can answer them later to see if you have learned the material well. You can also enlist the help of friends, study partners, or family (if they are willing to do this for you). You can also study alone. Some people make flash cards for the anatomy portion of the course. It is a good idea to do this for the muscle section, but you may be able to get most of the information down by using the preceding technique. Flash cards take time to fill out, so use them carefully.

Use memory devices for complex material. A mnemonic device is a memory phrase that has some relationship to the study material. For example, there are two bones in the wrist right next to one another, the trapezium and the trapezoid. The mnemonic device used by one student was that trapez*ium* rhymes with th*umb* and it is the one under the thumb.

Use your study group as a support group. A good study group is very effective in helping you do your best in class. Study with people who will push you to do your best. If you get discouraged, your study partners can be invaluable support people. A good group can help you improve your test scores, develop study hints, encourage you to do your best, and let you know that you are not the *only* one living, eating, and breathing anatomy and physiology.

Just as a good study group can really help, a bad group can drag you down farther than you might go on your own. If you are in a group that constantly complains about the instructor, that the class is too hard, that there is too much work, that the tests are not fair, that you don't really need to know this much anatomy and physiology for your field of study, and that this isn't medical school, then get yourself out of that group and into one excited by the information. Don't listen to people who complain constantly and make up excuses instead of studying. There is a tendency to start believing the complaints, and that begins a cycle of failure. Get out of a bad situation early and get with a group that will move forward.

Do well in the class and you will feel good about the experience. If you set up a study time with a group of people and they spend most of the time talking about parties, sports, or personal problems, then you aren't studying. There is nothing wrong with talking about parties, sports, or helping someone with personal problems, but you need to address the task at hand, learning anatomy and physiology. Don't feel bad if you must get out of your study group. It is *your* education, and if your partners don't want to study, then they don't really care about your academic well-being. A good study partner is one who pays attention in class, who is prepared ahead of the study time session, and who can explain information that you may have gotten wrong in your notes. You may want to get the phone number of two or three such classmates.

Test-Taking

Finally, you need to take quizzes and exams in a successful manner. By doing practice tests, you can develop confidence. Do well early in the semester. Study extra hard early (there is no such thing as overstudying!).

If you fail the first test or quiz, then you must work yourself out of an emotional ditch. Study early and consistently, and then spend the evening before the exam going over the material in a general way and solving those last few problems. Some people do succeed under pressure and cram before exams; however, the information is stored in short-term memory and does not serve them well in their major field! If you study on a routine basis, then you can get up on the morning of a test, have a good breakfast, listen to some encouraging music, maybe review a bit, and be ready for the exam.

Your instructor is there to help you learn anatomy and physiology, and this laboratory manual was written with you in mind. Relate as much of the material as you can to your body and keep an optimistic attitude.

Please feel free to write me or e-mail me with your comments, suggestions, and criticisms. I value your input and hope that your comments will lead to an even better seventh edition of this laboratory manual.

Eric Wise
Santa Barbara City College
721 Cliff Drive
Santa Barbara, CA 93109
wise@sbcc.edu

EXERCISE

21

LABORATORY

The Brain and Cranial Nerves

INTRODUCTION

Two specific traits distinguish humans from other animals. One is our upright posture, and the other is the extensive development of our brain. In this exercise you examine the anatomy of the human brain and the cranial nerves associated with it. You also compare the human brain to a sheep brain and note similarities and differences. Not only is there a difference in the size of the brains between humans and sheep but also a difference in the relative size of various structures of the brain and the position of some of the anatomy of the brain. You may want to review the planes of sectioning in Exercise 2.

The brain, part of the central nervous system, is located in the cranial cavity of the skull and weighs approximately 1.4 kilograms (3 pounds). The brain is derived from three embryonic regions, each of which further develops into more specific areas. The three embryonic regions of the brain are the **prosencephalon,** or **forebrain;** the **mesencephalon,** or **midbrain;** and the **rhombencephalon,** or **hindbrain.** Cranial nerves, though belonging to the peripheral nervous system, are studied along with the brain, as they are closely associated with it. Knowledge of the anatomy of the brain is important in locating the cranial nerves. These topics are covered in the Saladin text in chapter 14, "The Brain and Cranial Nerves."

OBJECTIVES

At the end of this exercise you should be able to

1. name the three meninges of the brain and their location relative to one another;
2. locate the three major regions of the brain;
3. name the main structures in each of the three regions of the brain;
4. describe the function of the major structures in the brain;
5. trace the path of cerebrospinal fluid through the brain;
6. list the major blood vessels that take blood to or from the brain.

MATERIALS

Models and charts of the human brain

Preserved human brains (if available)

Cast of the ventricles of the brain

Chart, section, or illustration of the brain in coronal and transverse sections

Sheep brains

Dissection trays

Scalpels or razor blades

Gloves

Blunt probes

PROCEDURE

Meninges

There are three membranes, called **meninges,** that surround the brain. The outermost of these is the **dura mater** (DOO-rah MAH-tur; Latin for "tough mother"), a tough, dense connective tissue membrane that encircles the brain and has a series of shelves that extend into the brain. The next deeper layer is the **arachnoid** (uh-RAK-noyd; Greek for spider web–like) **mater,** a thin membrane. Between the dura mater and the arachnoid membrane is the subdural space. Deep to the arachnoid is the **subarachnoid space,** which contains **cerebrospinal fluid (CSF).** The deepest layer is the **pia** (PEE-uh; Latin for soft) **mater,** a membrane directly on the outer surface of the brain. Locate the meninges in preserved brains in the lab (if available) and compare them to figure 21.1.

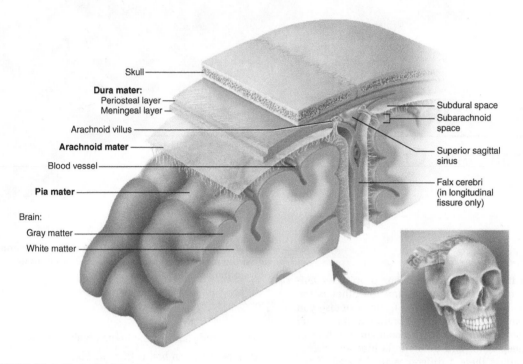

FIGURE 21.1 **Meninges of the Brain**

Overview of the Brain

The major regions of the brain can be subdivided into smaller areas. The forebrain is the largest region of the brain and consists primarily of the cerebrum and the diencephalon (see table 21.1 and figure 21.2). The midbrain is the smallest region of the brain and is located between the forebrain and the hindbrain. The hindbrain is composed of the pons, the medulla oblongata (me-DULL-ah OB-long-GAH-ta) and the cerebellum. The hindbrain is the most inferior portion of the brain and connects to the spinal cord at the level of the foramen magnum.

Blood Supply to the Brain

The blood vessels that supply nutrients and oxygen to the brain do not penetrate the brain tissue but form a meshwork around the brain and into the open spaces in the interior. The main arteries that provide blood to the brain are the **vertebral arteries** and the **internal carotid arteries.** Locate the vertebral arteries as illustrated in figure 21.3. These arteries pass through the transverse foramina of the cervical vertebrae and join to form the **basilar artery** at the base of the brain before branching into the **arterial circle** (circle of Willis) that forms a loop around the pituitary gland. The basilar artery gives rise to the **cerebellar** (SER-eh-BEL-ur) **arteries,** which take blood to the cerebellum. A pair of vessels joins the arterial circle at the anterior end, and these are the internal carotid

TABLE 21.1	Regions of the Brain
Forebrain	*Midbrain*
Telencephalon	Peduncles
Cerebrum (cerebral hemispheres)	Tectum
Cerebral cortex (gray matter)	Corpora quadrigemina
Basal nuclei (gray matter)	Superior colliculus
Corpus callosum	Inferior colliculus
Diencephalon	*Hindbrain*
Pineal body	Metencephalon
Thalamus	Pons
Hypothalamus	Cerebellum
Pituitary gland	Myelencephalon
Mammillary bodies	Medulla oblongata

arteries. From the arterial circle numerous **cerebral** (seh-REE-bral) **arteries** take blood superiorly to the surface of the cerebrum and into the interior of the brain. These lead to capillaries where an exchange of blood gases, nutrients, and waste material takes place between the cardiovascular system and the specialized brain cells. Note the various arteries in figure 21.3 at the base of the brain.

The drainage of the brain occurs as veins take blood from the brain and pass through the subarachnoid membrane

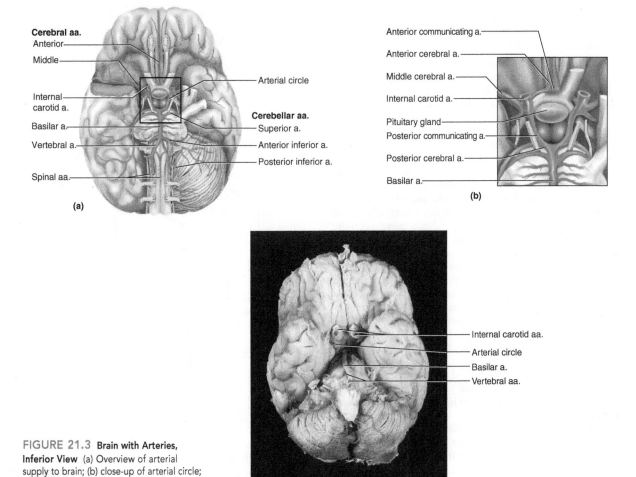

Telencephalon —┐
            ├— Forebrain
Diencephalon —┘

Mesencephalon ─┤— Midbrain

Pons ─┐
      ├— Metencephalon
Cerebellum ─┘

Myelencephalon
(medulla oblongata)

Spinal cord

Hindbrain

FIGURE 21.2 Major Regions of the Brain

Cerebral aa.
Anterior
Middle

Internal
carotid a.

Basilar a.

Vertebral a.

Spinal aa.

Arterial circle

Cerebellar aa.
Superior a.
Anterior inferior a.
Posterior inferior a.

(a)

Anterior communicating a.
Anterior cerebral a.
Middle cerebral a.
Internal carotid a.
Pituitary gland
Posterior communicating a.
Posterior cerebral a.
Basilar a.

(b)

Internal carotid aa.
Arterial circle
Basilar a.
Vertebral aa.

(c)

FIGURE 21.3 Brain with Arteries, Inferior View (a) Overview of arterial supply to brain; (b) close-up of arterial circle; (c) photograph.

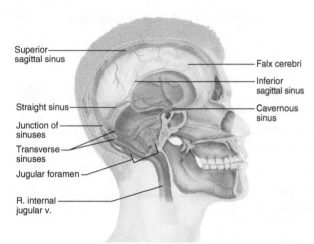

Superior sagittal sinus
Falx cerebri
Inferior sagittal sinus
Straight sinus
Cavernous sinus
Junction of sinuses
Transverse sinuses
Jugular foramen
R. internal jugular v.

FIGURE 21.4 Major Venous Drainage of the Brain

to the **venous sinuses** in the subdural spaces. The drainage of blood from the brain flows into the **internal jugular veins** on the return trip to the heart. Examine figure 21.4 for the venous drainage from the brain.

Ventricles of the Brain

The hollow neural tube that develops in the first trimester of pregnancy becomes the ventricles of the brain in the adult. The two ventricles that occupy the center of each cerebral hemisphere are known as the **lateral ventricles.** These ventricles receive **cerebrospinal fluid** from tufts of blood capillaries called **choroid** (CO-royd) **plexuses.** In preserved brains the choroid plexuses are small, brown areas at the superior portions of the ventricles. Fluid from the lateral ventricles flows through the **interventricular foramina** (foramina of Monro) and into the **third ventricle.** The third ventricle occurs in the thalamus and receives CSF from choroid plexuses in that area. The third ventricle drains into the **fourth ventricle** by way of the **mesencephalic** (MEZ-en-she-FAHL-ik) **(cerebral) aqueduct.** If this duct becomes occluded, then CSF accumulates in the lateral and third ventricles. This increases the size of the ventricles, producing a condition known as **hydrocephaly.** Normally, the mesencephalic aqueduct is open and passes through the region of the midbrain. Posterior to the mesencephalic aqueduct is the fourth ventricle, which occupies a space anterior to the cerebellum. The fourth ventricle also has a choroid plexus that secretes CSF. Cerebrospinal fluid flows from the fourth ventricle to the central canal of the spinal cord, into the subarachnoid space of the spinal cord and brain. The CSF cushions and provides buoyancy to the brain. CSF flows through the arachnoid granulations under the dura mater of the skull to the venous sinuses, and the fluid returns to the rest of the cardiovascular system by the **internal jugular veins.** There are approximately 150 mL of CSF in the central nervous system, and it takes about 6 hours to circulate through the system. Locate the ventricles of the brain in figure 21.5.

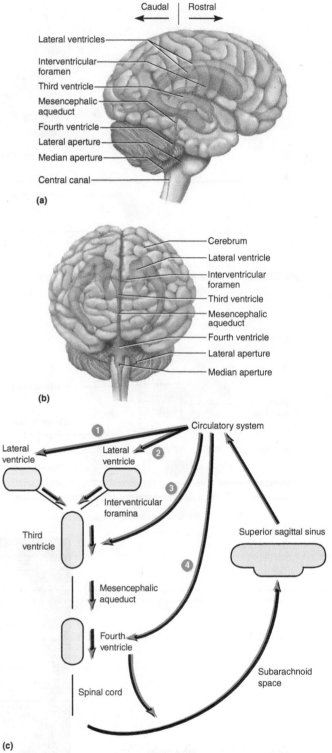

Caudal | Rostral

(a)
Lateral ventricles
Interventricular foramen
Third ventricle
Mesencephalic aqueduct
Fourth ventricle
Lateral aperture
Median aperture
Central canal

(b)
Cerebrum
Lateral ventricle
Interventricular foramen
Third ventricle
Mesencephalic aqueduct
Fourth ventricle
Lateral aperture
Median aperture

(c)
Circulatory system
Lateral ventricle
Lateral ventricle
Interventricular foramina
Third ventricle
Superior sagittal sinus
Mesencephalic aqueduct
Fourth ventricle
Spinal cord
Subarachnoid space

FIGURE 21.5 Ventricles of the Brain (a) Lateral view; (b) anterior view; (c) schematic presentation of the flow of cerebrospinal fluid. Numbers 1–4 represent flow through choroid plexuses.

Surface View of the Brain

Examine a model or chart of the brain and locate the **forebrain** and the **hindbrain.** In the forebrain you should examine the large **cerebrum,** which can be seen with folds and ridges known as **convolutions,** which increase the surface area of the brain. The ridges of the convolutions are called **gyri** (JY-rye; singular, *gyrus*), and the depressions are either **sulci** (SUL-sye; singular, *sulcus*) or **fissures.** Fissures are deeper than sulci. The lateral view of the brain allows you to see the major lobes of each cerebral hemisphere. These lobes are named for the bones of the skull under which they lie. They are the **frontal, parietal, occipital,** and **temporal lobes.** The **lateral fissure** (sulcus) separates the temporal lobe from the frontal and parietal lobes of the brain. You can locate these features in figure 21.6.

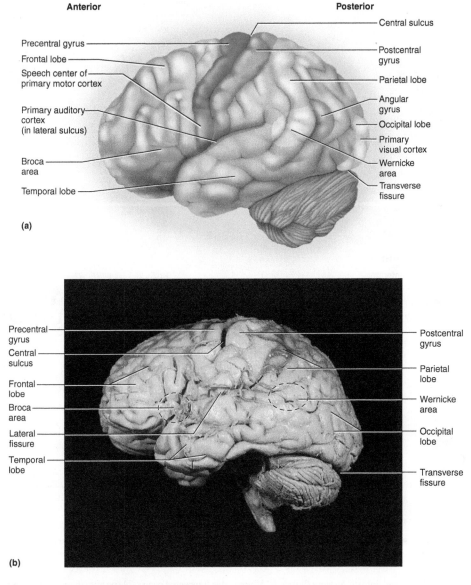

FIGURE 21.6 **Brain, Lateral View** (a) Diagram; (b) photograph.

Frontal Lobe

The **frontal lobe** is responsible for many of the higher functions associated with being human. The frontal lobe is involved in intellect, abstract reasoning, creativity, social awareness, and language. An important area responsible for controlling the formation of speech is called the **Broca area,** or the **motor speech area.** This region is located on the left side of the brain in most people, whether they are right-handed or left-handed. This area controls the muscles involved in speech. It is usually located in the left frontal lobe. Locate the frontal lobe in figure 21.6. The posterior border of the frontal lobe is defined by the **central sulcus.**

To find the central sulcus, look for two convolutions that run from the superior portion of the cerebrum to the lateral fissure, more or less continuously. The gyrus anterior to the central sulcus is part of the frontal lobe and is known as the **precentral gyrus,** or the **primary motor cortex.** By constructing an image of the body on the brain, this figure produces the image of a person known as a homunculus. A **motor homunculus** (hoh-MUNK-you-lus) is seen in figure 21.7a. How much of the precentral gyrus is dedicated to the face?

How much of the gyrus is dedicated to the hands?

How much is dedicated to the trunk?

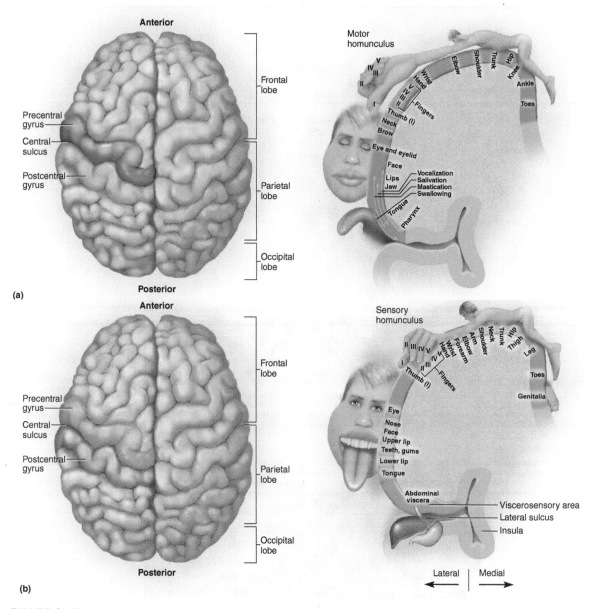

FIGURE 21.7 **Primary Motor and Somatic Sensory Cortex** (a) Motor cortex (precentral gyrus); (b) somatic sensory cortex (postcentral gyrus).

Parietal Lobe

The gyrus posterior to the central sulcus is known as the **postcentral gyrus,** or the **primary somatic sensory cortex.** This is part of the parietal lobe and is involved in receiving somatic sensory information from the body. This area has also been mapped, and you can see a **sensory homunculus** represented in figure 21.7*b.* The primary sensory cortex receives information, yet the material is integrated just posterior to the sensory cortex in the **association areas.** The primary sensory cortex pinpoints the part of the body affected, and the association area interprets the type of sensation (pain, heat, cold, etc.). Locate the structures of the parietal lobe in figure 21.6.

The **Wernicke** (WUR-ni-keh) **area** is involved in the formation of language, such as the recognition of written and spoken language and in the forming of coherent sentences. The Wernicke area extends into the temporal lobe as well.

Occipital Lobe

Posterior to the parietal lobe is the **occipital lobe** of the brain. The occipital lobe is considered the primary visual area of the brain, and damage to this lobe can lead to blindness. Shape, color, and distance of an object are perceived here. Recollection of past visual images occurs here as well. As you are reading these words your occipital lobe is receiving the information and transferring it to other regions, which convert the words to thought. Between the occipital lobe and the cerebellum is a **transverse fissure** that separates these two regions of

the brain. Locate the occipital lobe and the cerebellum in figure 21.6.

Temporal Lobe

The **temporal lobe** is separated from the frontal and parietal lobes by the **lateral fissure** (sulcus). The temporal lobe contains an area known as the **primary auditory cortex,** which interprets hearing impulses sent from the inner ear. This auditory cortex distinguishes the nature of the sound (music, noise, speech) and the location, distance, pitch, and rhythm. The primary auditory cortex translates words into thought. The temporal lobe also has centers for the sense of smell **(olfactory centers)** and taste **(gustatory centers).** Deep to the temporal lobe is a small mass of cortical material called the insula.

Cerebral Hemispheres

Rotate the brain so that you are looking at it from a superior view, and find the **longitudinal fissure** that separates the cerebrum into the left and right cerebral hemispheres. The **left cerebral hemisphere** in most people is involved in language and reasoning. For example, the Broca area is typically on the left side of the brain. The **right cerebral hemisphere** of the brain is involved in space and pattern perceptions, artistic awareness, imagination, and music comprehension. This specialization where one hemisphere of the cerebrum is involved in a particular task is known as **cerebral asymmetry,** or **hemispheric dominance.** Examine the surface features of the brain in figure 21.8.

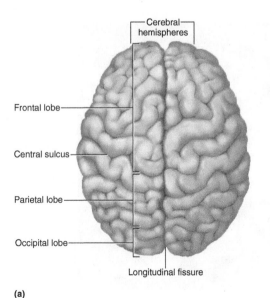

(a)

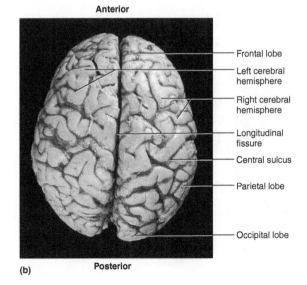

(b)

FIGURE 21.8 **Brain, Superior View** (a) Diagram; (b) photograph.

Inferior Aspect of the Brain

Forebrain

Examine the frontal and temporal lobes of the cerebrum. You may be able to see the **pituitary gland** if it has not been removed. The **optic chiasma** (KYE-as-muh) (*chiasma* = cross) is anterior to the pituitary and transmits visual impulses from the eyes to the brain. Two small processes posterior to the pituitary are the **mammillary bodies,** which relay information from the limbic system to the fornix.

Hindbrain

From an inferior view of the brain locate the **pons, medulla oblongata,** and **cerebellum** (SER-eh-BEL-um). The cerebellum has much finer folds of neural tissue called **folia.** The medulla oblongata is located inferior to the cerebellum. The medulla oblongata has centers for respiratory rate control, control of blood pressure, and other vital centers. Some information from the right side of the body crosses over to the left brain in the medulla oblongata. Information coming from the left side of the body crosses over to the right side of the brain. The area where motor tracts cross over in the medulla is known as the **decussation of the pyramids.** A stroke on the right side of the brain might affect the muscle activity on the left side of the body. The medulla oblongata terminates at the foramen magnum and the cervical region of the spinal cord continues inferior to the foramen magnum. The enlarged portion of the brain anterior to the medulla is the pons, which is a relay center for information. Examine these structures of the brain in figure 21.9.

Midsagittal Section of the Brain

Forebrain

Examine a midsagittal section of a brain, as illustrated in figure 21.10. This section is seen by cutting the brain through the longitudinal fissure. Locate the C-shaped **corpus callosum,** which connects the two cerebral hemispheres. The posterior portion of the corpus callosum is known as the **splenium,** and the anterior portion is the **genu.** Just inferior to the corpus callosum is the **septum pellucidum,** which separates the lateral ventricles of the brain. If the septum pellucidum is missing, you will be able to look into the lateral ventricle without obstruction. Locate these structures in figure 21.10.

Examine the material in the lab and locate the **diencephalon,** which consists of, in part, the thalamus and the hypothalamus. The **thalamus** forms the lateral wall around the third ventricle and is a relay center that receives almost all the sensory information from the body and projects it to the cerebral cortex.

Below the thalamus is the **hypothalamus,** which has numerous autonomic centers. The hypothalamus, in part, directs the ANS and is involved with the **pituitary gland** (in the hypothalamopituitary axis) in many endocrine functions. Centers for thirst, water balance, pleasure, rage, sexual desire, hunger, sleep patterns, temperature, and aggression are located in the hypothalamus.

You should also be able to locate the **mammillary bodies** on the inferior portion of the diencephalon and the **optic chiasma** just anterior to it. The **pineal gland** is located posterior to the thalamus and is an endocrine gland that secretes melatonin, a hormone that regulates daily

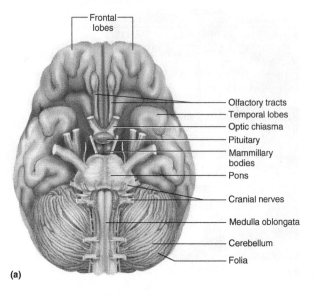

(a)

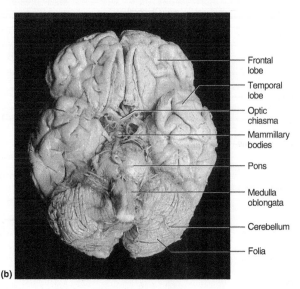

(b)

FIGURE 21.9 Brain, Inferior View (a) Diagram; (b) photograph.

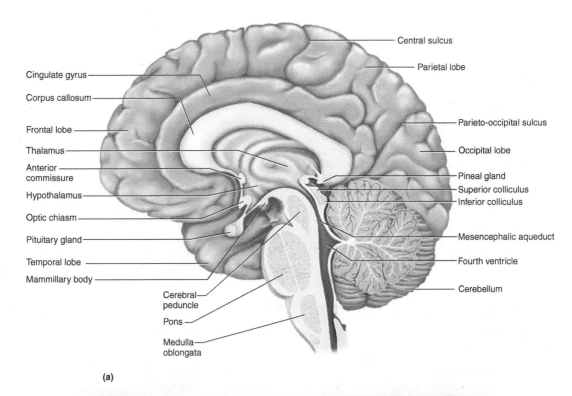

(a)

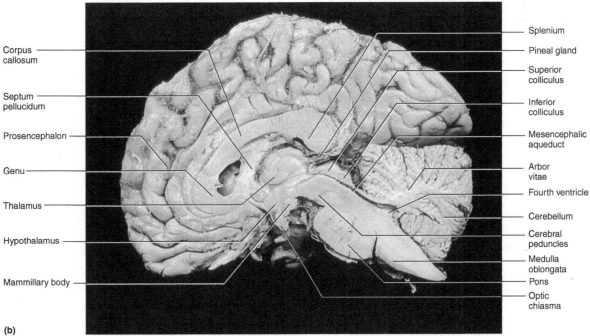

(b)

FIGURE 21.10 **Brain, Midsagittal Section** (a) Diagram; (b) photograph.

286   **LABORATORY 21** The Brain and Cranial Nerves

rhythms. Both the pineal gland and the pituitary gland are covered more in depth in Laboratory Exercise 28.

Midbrain

The midbrain is a small area posterior to the diencephalon. This small area consists of the **cerebral peduncles,** which occupy an area anterior to the pons and on the ventral surface of the brain. The **mesencephalic (cerebral) aqueduct** passes through the mesencephalon, with the **peduncles** being inferior and the **tectum** as a roof superior to the aqueduct. Locate these features in the material in the lab and in figure 21.10. Superior to the tectum are four hemispheric processes known as the **corpora quadrigemina,** which consist of the **superior colliculi** (col-LIC-youlye; areas of visual reflexes) and the **inferior colliculi** (areas of auditory reflexes). The midbrain also houses a center known as the **substantia nigra** (sub-STAN-she-uh NY-gruh; not seen in midsagittal sections) that, when not functioning properly, causes Parkinson's disease.

Hindbrain

The **hindbrain** consists of an anterior bulge known as the **pons,** a terminal **medulla oblongata,** and the highly convoluted **cerebellum** (see figure 21.10). The pons carries sensory information from the inferior regions of the body to the thalamus. The pons has important respiratory centers involved in controlling breathing rate.

The cerebellum is a location noted for muscle coordination, the maintenance of posture, the conceptualization of the passage of time, and other cognitive functions.

The cerebellum consists of an outer **cerebellar cortex** and an inner, extensively branched pattern of white matter known as the **arbor vitae.** The **folia** of the cerebellum can be seen in this section. The triangular space anterior to the cerebellum is the fourth ventricle and can be seen in figure 21.10. Examine the features of the hindbrain as described here and seen in material in the lab.

Coronal Section of the Brain

The brain consists of **unmyelinated** gray matter and **myelinated** white matter. The **gray matter** of the brain is extensive and forms the **cerebral cortex.** Most of the active, integrative processes of the brain occur in the cerebral cortex (see figure 21.11). The cerebral cortex is approximately 4 mm thick and occupies the superficial regions of the brain. The cortex is where humans do most of their "thinking." It is the main metabolic area of the brain. Young adults have perhaps 50 billion neurons in the cerebral cortex. Deep to the cortex is the **white matter** of the brain, which consists of **tracts** that take information from deeper regions of the brain to the cerebral cortex for processing. Tracts in the CNS are myelinated fibers and function as nerves do in the PNS. Sensory information coming from the spinal cord moves through the inferior regions of the brain and through the white matter for integration in the cerebral cortex. White matter can also take information from one region of the cerebral cortex to another for integration or from the cerebral cortex back to the spinal cord and to other parts of the body for action.

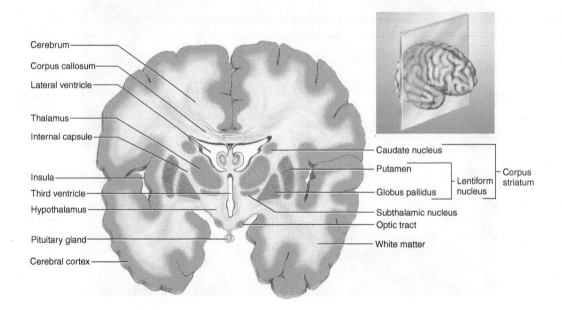

FIGURE 21.11 **Brain, Coronal Section**

Gray matter is not restricted to the cerebral cortex, however. Deep islands of gray matter in the brain compose the **basal nuclei (basal ganglia)**, such as the **caudate nucleus, putamen,** and **globus pallidus.** Basal nuclei serve a number of functions in the brain, many of which involve subconscious processes, such as the swinging of arms while walking or the regulation of muscle tone. Basal nuclei are found not only in the cerebrum but in the thalamus and midbrain as well.

Limbic System

Part of the limbic system can be seen in a coronal section. The limbic system is a complex region of the brain involved in mood and emotion and has centers for feeding, sexual desire, fear, and satisfaction. The inferior portion of the limbic system has neural fibers that come from the olfactory regions of the brain. These are best seen in a model of the limbic system or in a transected brain. Examine figure 21.12 for the major features of the limbic system.

Brainstem

The brainstem consists of the brain, excluding the cerebrum and cerebellum. Look at a model or section of brain that has had the cerebrum removed. Locate the corpora quadrigemina (see figure 21.13) along with the medulla oblongata and the pons.

Development of the Central Nervous System

The brain begins development, as does the rest of the nervous system, in the third week of pregnancy as a **neural groove** in the ectoderm. By the fourth week the brain has folded into a **neural tube** that contains the **central canal**

(see figure 21.14). The posterior portion of the central canal becomes the central canal of the spinal cord. The anterior portion of the canal becomes the ventricles of the brain in adults. By the sixth week of development the cerebral hemispheres have begun to form and continue their development throughout pregnancy.

Cranial Nerves

The cranial nerves are part of the PNS but they are covered with the brain in lab as they are closely associated with it. There are 12 pairs of cranial nerves. The cranial nerves are listed by Roman numeral, and you should know the nerve by name and by number. Examine a model of the brain along with figure 21.15; the cranial nerves, except for nerve XII, are in sequence from anterior to posterior. When you study nerves you should examine the anatomy of the brain to see where the nerve emerges from the brain. If you know, for example, that the abducens is found between the pons and the medulla oblongata, then you can use that nerve as a way to locate other nerves. If the predominant function of the nerve is to receive neural input then the nerve is considered a **sensory nerve.** If the predominant function of the nerve is to innervate muscles then the nerve is considered a **motor nerve.** Some nerves have significant sensory and motor functions, and these are **mixed nerves.**

The **olfactory nerve** runs along the anterior base of the brain at the inferior aspect of the frontal lobe. The **optic nerve** (*optic* refers to sight) is a sensory nerve from the eye to the base of the brain and forms the optic chiasma. Some tracts remain on one side of the brain, while others cross to the other side. The **oculomotor nerve** is anterior to the pons, more or less in the midline of the brain, while the **trochlear nerve** emerges at about

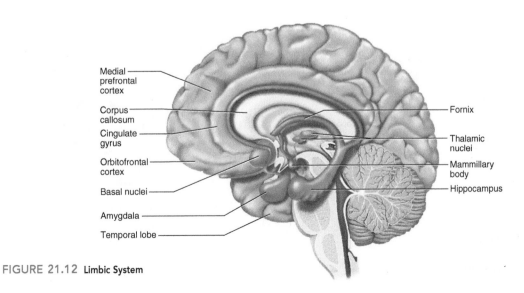

Medial prefrontal cortex
Corpus callosum
Cingulate gyrus
Orbitofrontal cortex
Basal nuclei
Amygdala
Temporal lobe
Fornix
Thalamic nuclei
Mammillary body
Hippocampus

FIGURE 21.12 **Limbic System**

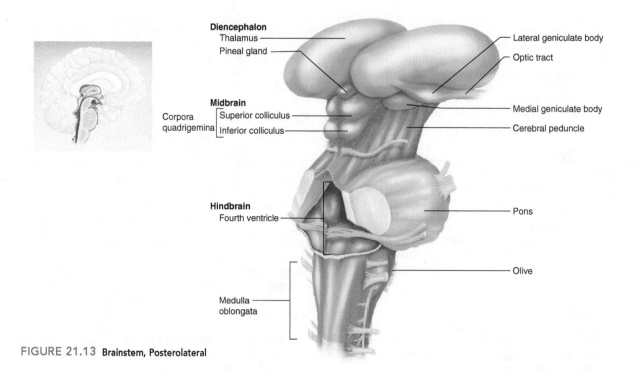

FIGURE 21.13 **Brainstem, Posterolateral**

a 45-degree angle from midline on the lateral aspect of the pons. The large **trigeminal nerve** is found at a 90-degree angle to the pons and is located on the lateral aspect of the pons. The **abducens nerve** is located at the midline junction of the pons and medulla oblongata, while the **facial nerve** is more lateral. Posterior to the **facial nerve** is the **vestibulocochlear nerve,** and the nerve directly behind that is the **glossopharyngeal nerve.** The **vagus nerve** (*vagus* = wandering) is a large nerve or large cluster of fibers, and on the lateral aspect of the medulla oblongata is the **accessory nerve.** More toward the midline is the **hypoglossal nerve,** the last of the cranial nerves. Locate these nerves in figure 21.15 and note their details in tables 21.2 and 21.3.

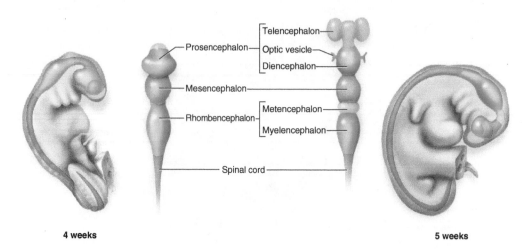

4 weeks   **5 weeks**

FIGURE 21.14 **Brain Development**

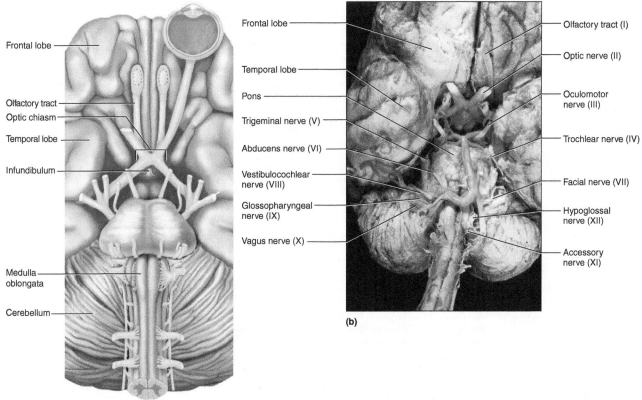

(a)

(b)

FIGURE 21.15 Cranial Nerves, Inferior View (a) Diagram; (b) photograph.

TABLE 21.2		Cranial Nerves—Function
Number	**Name**	**Function**
I	Olfactory	Receives sensory information from the nose
II	Optic	Receives sensory information from the eye, transmitting the sense of vision to the brain
III	Oculomotor	Transmits motor information to move the eye muscles particularly to the medial, superior, and inferior rectus muscles and to the inferior oblique muscle
IV	Trochlear	Transmits motor information to move the eye muscles, particularly the superior oblique muscle
V	Trigeminal	A three-branched nerve; transmits both sensory information from, and motor information to, the head
VI	Abducens	A motor nerve to move the eye muscles, particularly the lateral rectus muscle
VII	Facial	A large nerve that receives sensory information from the anterior tongue and takes motor information to the head muscles
VIII	Vestibulocochlear	Receives sensory information from the ear; the vestibular part transmits equilibrium information and the cochlear part transmits acoustic information
IX	Glossopharyngeal	A mixed nerve of the tongue and throat that receives information on taste
X	Vagus	Receives sensory information from the abdomen, thorax, neck, and root of the tongue; transmits motor information to the pharynx and larynx and controls autonomic functions of the heart, digestive organs, spleen, and kidneys
XI	Accessory	A motor nerve to the muscles of the neck that move the head
XII	Hypoglossal	A motor nerve to the tongue

TABLE 21.3		Cranial Nerves—Location
Number	**Name**	**Location**
I	Olfactory	Begin in the upper nasal cavity and pass through the cribriform plate of the ethmoid bone. They synapse in the olfactory bulbs on each side of the longitudinal fissure of the brain. The fibers take information on the sense of smell and pass through the olfactory tracts to be interpreted in the temporal lobe of the brain.
II	Optic	Take sensory information from the retina at the back of the eye and transmit the impulses through the optic canal in the sphenoid bone. Some fibers cross at the optic chiasm and pass via the optic tracts to the occipital lobe, where vision is interpreted.
III	Oculomotor	Emerge from the surface of the brain near the midline and just anterior to the pons. They pass through the superior orbital fissure and innervate the inferior oblique muscle and the medial, superior, and inferior rectus muscles and carry parasympathetic fibers to the lens and iris.
IV	Trochlear	Seen at the sides of the pons at about a 45-degree angle from the midline of the brain. They pass through the superior orbital fissure to the superior oblique muscle.
V	Trigeminal	Seen at a 90-degree angle from the midline at the lateral sides of the pons. The trigeminal has three branches: (1) the ophthalmic branch passes through the superior orbital fissure; (2) the maxillary branch passes through the foramen rotundum of the sphenoid bone; (3) the mandibular branch passes through the foramen ovale of the sphenoid bone and enters the mandible by the mandible foramen and exits by the mental foramen.
VI	Abducens	Begins at the midline junction between the pons and the medulla oblongata and passes through the superior orbital fissure to carry motor information to the lateral rectus muscle of the eye.
VII	Facial	Begins as the first of a cluster of nerves on the anterolateral part of the medulla oblongata. It passes through the internal auditory meatus and through the inner ear to the stylomastoid foramen of the temporal bone to innervate facial muscles and glands. It receives sensory information from the anterior tongue. Sensory information of the tongue is interpreted in the temporal lobe of the brain.
VIII	Vestibulocochlear	Comes from the inner ear and passes through the internal auditory meatus. The conduction passes to the pons, and hearing and balance are interpreted in the temporal lobe.
IX	Glossopharyngeal	Passes through the jugular foramen to innervate muscles of the throat (pharyngeal branches) and the tongue (glossal branches). Motor portions of the nerve control some muscles of swallowing and salivary glands, while sensory nerves receive information from the posterior tongue and from baroreceptors of the carotid artery.
X	Vagus	Passes through the jugular foramen and along the neck to the larynx, heart, and abdominal region. The sensory impulses travel in this nerve from the viscera in the abdomen, the thorax, the neck, and the root of the tongue to the brain.
XI	Accessory	Multiple fibers arise from the lateral sides of the medulla oblongata and pass through the jugular foramen to numerous muscles of the neck.
XII	Hypoglossal	Begins at the anterior surface of the medulla and passes through the hypoglossal canal to innervate the muscles of the tongue.

TABLE 21.4		Type of Cranial Nerves		
Number	**Name**	**Name Mnemonic**	**Type**	**Mnemonic**
I	Olfactory	Old	Sensory	Sally
II	Optic	Oliver	Sensory	Sells
III	Oculomotor	Ogg	Motor*	Many
IV	Trochlear	Traveled	Motor	Mangoes
V	Trigeminal	Through	Both	But
VI	Abducens	Arches	Motor	My
VII	Facial	For	Both	Brother
VIII	Vestibulocochlear	Very	Sensory	Sells
IX	Glossopharyngeal	Good	Both	Bigger
X	Vagus	Vacations	Both	Better
XI	Accessory	And	Motor	Mega
XII	Hypoglossal	Holidays	Motor	Mangoes

*Motor nerves have sensory fibers that come from proprioreceptors in the muscles they innervate. Information about the tension of the muscle is sent back to the brain to make adjustments in contractile rate. Since the main function of these nerves is motor, they are listed as motor nerves, even though they have some sensory capabilities.

The cranial nerves are listed in table 21.4 as sensory nerves, motor nerves, or both sensory and motor nerves. There have been many mnemonic devices constructed to remember the sequence of cranial nerves. If you use the first letter of the name of the cranial nerve you can learn the sequence of these nerves. One such mnemonic is *Old Oliver Ogg Traveled Through Arches For Very Good Vacations And Holidays*. The first letters of the words in the mnemonic represent the first letters of the names of the nerves.

Dissection of the Sheep Brain

Take a sheep brain back to your table along with a dissecting tray and appropriate dissection tools. If the brains still have the **dura mater,** examine this tough connective tissue coat that occurs on the outside of the brain. Cut through this layer to examine the other meninges that occur underneath it. Deep to the dura mater is a

filmy layer of tissue that contains blood vessels. This is known as the **arachnoid mater.** If you tease some of the membrane away from the brain you will see that it has a cobweblike appearance in the **subarachnoid space.** The subarachnoid space may contain some fluid, the CSF. Deep to this layer and adhering directly to the brain convolutions is the **pia mater,** the surface lining of the convolutions of the brain. Work in pairs during the dissection of the sheep brain. Examine the features presented in the beginning of this exercise and locate the structures that appear in figure 21.16.

Find the major lobes of the brain, the cerebellum, pons, and medulla oblongata. Sheep are quadrupeds, and the flexure of the brain does not occur in them as it does in humans. Sheep have a horizontal spinal cord, while humans have a vertical one. The average weight of the sheep brain is about one-tenth that of humans. The greatest difference between the two is the larger cerebrum in humans, which reflects our greater cognitive abilities.

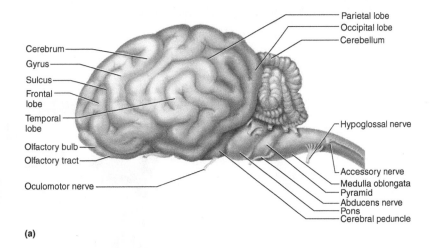

(a)

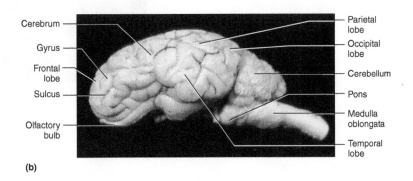

(b)

FIGURE 21.16 Brain of the Sheep, Lateral View (a) Diagram; (b) photograph.

292   **LABORATORY 21**   The Brain and Cranial Nerves

The pons in humans is larger due to increased neural transmission to and from the enlarged cerebrum. Sheep have an excellent sense of smell, and this is reflected in their larger olfactory bulbs. Examine the inferior surface of the sheep brain. You should see the olfactory bulbs and tracts, the optic nerve, and the optic chiasma easily from this view. The pituitary gland will probably not be attached but you should locate the infundibulum, caudad (posterior) to the optic chiasma. Locate these structures in figure 21.17. If the sheep brain is intact, you will need to decide which brain will be sectioned in the midsagittal plane and which will be sectioned in the coronal plane. For the midsagittal section, divide the brain along the length of the longitudinal fissure. Your cut should reflect a section illustrated in figure 21.18. Locate the corpus callosum, lateral ventricles, third ventricle, hypothalamus, pineal gland, superior and inferior colliculi, cerebellum, arbor vitae, pons, medulla oblongata, mesencephalic aqueduct, and fourth ventricle.

The coronal section of a sheep brain is illustrated in figure 21.19. After making a coronal section about midway through the cerebrum, you should locate the cerebral cortex, cerebral medulla, lateral ventricles, corpus callosum, third ventricle, thalamus, and hypothalamus.

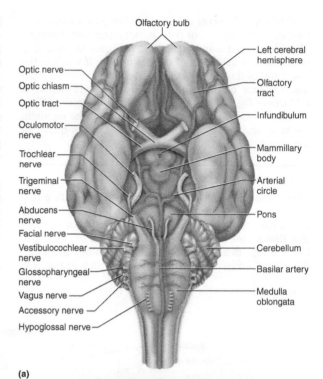

(a)

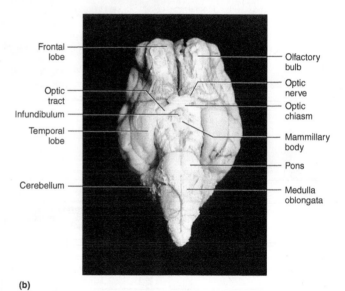

(b)

FIGURE 21.17 **Brain of the Sheep, Inferior View** (a) Diagram; (b) photograph.

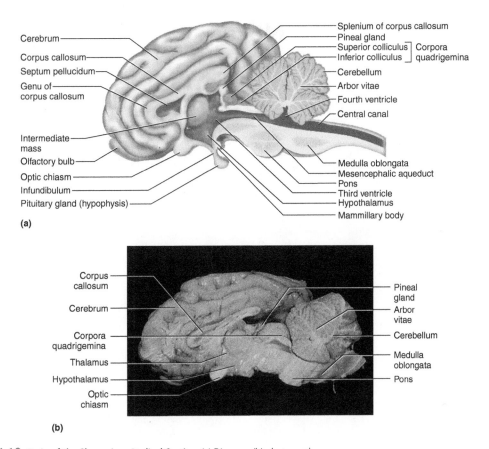

FIGURE 21.18 **Brain of the Sheep, Longitudinal Section** (a) Diagram; (b) photograph.

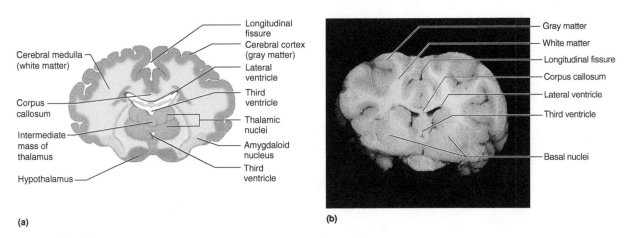

FIGURE 21.19 **Brain of the Sheep, Coronal Section** (a) Diagram; (b) photograph.

Notes

REVIEW SECTION ▦ connect
|ANATOMY & PHYSIOLOGY

The Brain and Cranial Nerves

Name ——————————————————————— *Date* ——————

Lab Section ——————————————————————— *Time* ——————

Review Questions

1. Which of the meninges is between the outer and inner meninges?

2. Name the major veins that take blood from the brain.

3. The basilic artery in the brain receives blood from what two arteries?

4. What fluid is found in the ventricles of the brain?

5. Where does fluid flow from the mesencephalic aqueduct?

6. a. What is the difference between a gyrus and a sulcus?

   b. What role do the convolutions play in the brain?

7. Name the lobes of the cerebrum.

8. What function does the precentral gyrus have?

9. What sense does the temporal lobe interpret?

10. What depression separates the temporal lobe from the parietal lobe?

11. What structure connects the cerebral hemispheres?

12. Name the major regions of the midbrain.

13. What function does the cerebellum have?

14. What function does the optic nerve have?

15. The trigeminal nerve is larger than the trochlear nerve. How does this correlate with the function of both nerves?

16. John pulled a "no-brainer" by hitting his forehead against the wall. What possible damage might he do to the function of his brain, particularly those functions associated with the frontal lobe?

17. If a stroke affected all the sensations interpreted by the brain just concerning the face and the hands, approximately what percentage of the postcentral gyrus would be affected?

18. One convenient excuse that people often make for their inability to do something is to describe themselves as left-brained or right-brained individuals. Describe what effect the loss of an entire cerebral hemisphere would have on specific functions, such as spatial awareness or the ability to speak.

19. Aphasia is loss of speech. Different types of aphasia can occur. If the Broca area were affected by a stroke, would the content of the spoken word be affected, or would the ability to pronounce words be affected?

20. Label the following illustration using the terms provided.

corpus callosum   arbor vitae
mesencephalic aqueduct   hypothalamus
pons   medulla oblongata
pineal gland   pituitary gland
thalamus   fourth ventricle

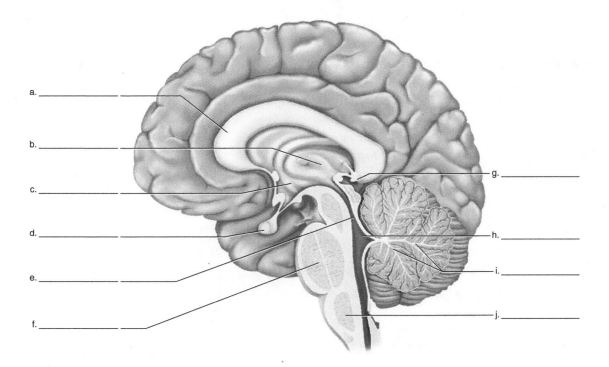

a. _____ _____

b. _____ _____

c. _____ _____

d. _____ _____

e. _____ _____

f. _____ _____

g. _____

h. _____

i. _____

j. _____

21. Label the following illustration using the terms provided.

olfactory nerves
trigeminal nerve
vagus nerve
medulla oblongata
hypoglossal nerves
pons
oculomotor nerve
cerebellum
optic nerve

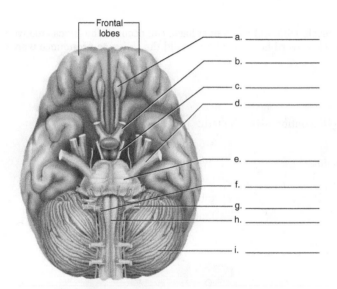

Frontal lobes

a. _____

b. _____

c. _____

d. _____

e. _____

f. _____

g. _____

h. _____

i. _____

22. Label the following illustration using the terms provided.

corpus callosum   arbor vitae
mesencephalic aqueduct   hypothalamus
pons   medulla oblongata
pineal gland   pituitary gland
thalamus   fourth ventricle

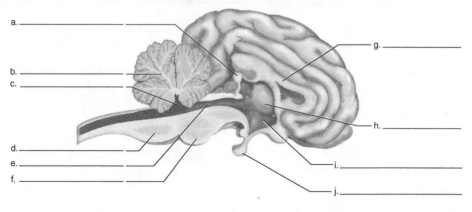

a. _____

b. _____

c. _____

g. _____

h. _____

d. _____

e. _____

f. _____

i. _____

j. _____

LABORATORY

Nervous System Physiology— Stimuli and Reflexes

INTRODUCTION

Neurons show two fundamental properties: excitability and conductivity. **Excitability** is the response of a nerve to some type of stimulus (chemical, mechanical, electrical), and **conductivity** is the transmission of a nerve impulse along the length of the neuron. When nerves are stimulated by chemical, mechanical, or electrical means, voltage-regulated gates open and send electrochemical currents (action potentials) along the length of the neuron. Nerves receive information from a particular area (sense organ, regions in the CNS, etc.) and carry signals to either the brain for interpretation or an effector for some type of action. Reflexes are vital for the body in order to respond to external or internal stimuli. Visceral reflexes (such as the adjustment of the pupil to changing light conditions) occur in smooth muscle, cardiac muscle, and glands and are not covered in this exercise. Somatic reflexes involve skeletal muscles and are part of reflex arcs in the body. The nature of nerve conduction and reflexes are covered in the Saladin text in chapter 12, "Nervous Tissue," and chapter 13, "The Spinal Cord, Spinal Nerves, and Somatic Reflexes." In this exercise you study the basic properties of neuronal conduction and their sensitivity to various stimuli and experiment with nerves as they form reflex arcs in several parts of the body.

OBJECTIVES

At the end of this exercise you should be able to

1. describe the threshold nature of nerve responses;
2. list three things that cause a nerve to be stimulated;
3. name one substance that stimulates nerves and one that inhibits them;
4. describe reflex arcs;
5. list all the parts of a monosynaptic and polysynaptic reflex arc;
6. define hyporeflexic and hyperreflexic.

MATERIALS

Nerve Physiology Section

Ph.I.L.S. CD

Compatible computer

Frogs

Latex or plastic gloves

Glass rod with hook at one end

Hot pad or mitt

Bunsen burner

Matches or flint lighter

Frog Ringer's solution in dropper bottles (see Appendix C)

Microscope slide or small glass plate

Filter paper or paper towel

Dissection equipment for live animals

Scalpel or scissors

Cotton sewing thread

Stimulator apparatus with probe

Myograph transducer

Physiograph or physiology computer

Five small (50 mL) beakers

5% sodium chloride solution

0.1% hydrochloric acid solution (1 mL of concentrated HCl in 1 liter of water)

Procaine hydrochloride solution

Cotton applicator sticks

Gauze squares

Ice bath

Reflex Section

Patellar reflex hammer

Rubber squeeze bulb

Models or charts of spinal cord and nerves

PROCEDURE Ph.I.L.S.

Virtual Experiments in Neurophysiology

Load the Physiology Interactive Lab Simulations (Ph.I.L.S.) disc. You will need a minimum of either a Windows XP, Vista or Pentium III computer or a Macintosh 10.2, G3 Processor and Adobe Flash 8.x Player to run the program.

For all of the virtual muscle experiments you should follow the standard procedures that come up when you open the CD.

1. Click on the number of the exercise that you want to complete. These are under the **Resting Potentials** or **Action Potentials** headings in the CD.

After you have selected your choice you should:

2. Read the objectives and introduction to the lab simulation. You can click on highlighted terms to see pictures or animations of the material in question.
3. Take the pre-lab quiz. If you get a question wrong, the program will let you know and provide you with the correct answer.
4. Click on the **Wet Lab** tab and read the material. The highlighted terms open up videos of an actual procedure.
5. Click on **Continue,** which opens up the **Laboratory Excercise**.
6. Perform the exercises as outlined below. Print out any information that your instructor directs after you have performed the experiment or download the information to a portable data storage device.
7. Take the post-lab quiz to determine your understanding of the lab.

The information for the specific lab exercises follows.

Resting Potentials 8. Resting Potential and External [K⁺]

Open the **Resting Potential and External [K⁺]** program and start the procedure by initiating a recording on the control panel. Insert the microelectrode into the muscle and then click on the Journal Entry to get an initial reading.

On the left side of the **Data Acquisition Unit** there is a black circle with a gray sphere in the middle. This is the micromanipulator. If you move the cursor over this area two arrows will show up. These are the up and down arrows, and they control the position of the microelectrode in the muscle. As you penetrate the muscle for the

first time you will see a change in the voltage on the right screen.

If you move the mouse to the left side of the Data Acquisition Unit you will bring up an "Overhead View" of the microelectrode in the muscle. If you continue to move the cursor to the left you will see two gray cylinders. These control where the microelectrode is moved in the muscle tissue. Every time you want to record data you must move the microelectrode to a new location. You must enter all the data in the journal for all of the concentrations of saline before you plot the graph.

What impact does increasing the potassium ion concentration have on membrane depolarization? Record your answer in the following space and in the review section at the end of the exercise.

? Effect of increasing potassium ion concentration:

_____ 1

Resting Potentials 9. Resting Potential and External [Na⁺]

Follow the same procedure as in number 8 on the CD-ROM for the **Resting Procedure and External Sodium Concentration** program. The setup is the same except that you will be increasing the sodium ion concentration rather than the potassium ion concentration.

Comparing the two solutions, which has a greater impact on membrane dynamics, sodium or potassium? Record your answer in the following space and in the review section at the end of the exercise.

? Greater impact on membrane dynamics: _____ 2

Action Potentials 10. The Compound Action Potential

Place all of the color-coded cables on the appropriate attachment points of the chamber holding the nerve. The drain tap is the small circular wheel located at the top of the chamber on the left-hand side. You must click and hold the knob in order for it to drain.

If you examine the graph you will see the stimulus on the left side of the graph followed by a compound action potential on the right. As with the muscle physiology experiment, if you move the cursor to the graph you will see crosshairs as you move the cursor. Place the crosshairs on the top of the curve and click. Click again on the baseline of the curve. When you click on the **Journal** icon it will enter the data into the journal.

You must click the "X" on the journal in order to proceed with obtaining more data. The threshold voltage is the voltage below which you get no response from the nerve. What was your threshold voltage? Record your answer in the following space and in the review section at the end of the exercise.

? Threshold voltage: _____ 3

Action Potentials 11. Conduction Velocity and Temperature
In this exercise you examine the speed of nerve conduction by altering the temperature of the nerve. The experiment runs at room temperature (22° C) and cold temperature (10° C). Follow the instructions as presented. Make sure that you click on both power buttons to turn on the equipment. Place all of the color-coded cables on the attachment points on the chamber holding the nerve. The tap is the small circular wheel located at the top of the chamber on the left-hand side. You must click and hold the knob in order for it to drain. After you run the first experiment at room temperature make sure that you enter your data into the journal by clicking on the **Journal** icon. Run the second experiment and compare the results of nerve conduction at different temperatures.

In which sequence (room temperature or cold) did you see a slowing down of the nerve conduction? Record your answer in the following space and in the review section at the end of the exercise.

❓ Slower nerve response: _____ 4

How does this response correlate with decreasing enzyme function based on temperature? Record your answer in the following space and in the review section at the end of the exercise.

❓ Correlation: _____ 5

Action Potential 12. The Refractory Period In the exercise, begin by increasing the voltage until there is no greater peak produced with increasing voltage. This value is the maximum recruitment for the nerve, and it means that all of the axons of the nerve are firing. With less voltage only some of the axons are firing and there is less of a response.

What is the maximum recruitment voltage that you obtained? Record your answer in the following space and in the review section at the end of the exercise.

❓ Maximum recruitment voltage: _____ 6

In the next section you can alter the frequency between the shocks and determine the absolute refractory period and the relative refractory period. Enter these data in the following space and in the review section at the end of the exercise.

❓ Absolute refractory period: _____ 7

❓ Relative refractory period: _____ 8

Review the structure of the neuron in Laboratory Exercise 20 for descriptions of the dendrites, nerve cell body, and axon and the anatomy of the nerve in Laboratory Exercise 22. Make sure you read through all of this exercise prior to beginning the experiments. Wear latex gloves as a general precaution when working with fresh specimens, such as frogs.

Frog Nerve Conduction

In the first part of this lab exercise you will determine if nerves respond to only a specific stimulus or if they are more general and respond to many stimuli. You will also determine if certain materials or environmental conditions inhibit nerve response.

In this exercise you observe the process of nerve impulse conduction by experimenting on frogs or by watching a demonstration, depending on the wishes of your instructor. If you experiment on frogs, obtain a doubly pithed frog, dissection equipment, frog Ringer's solution, and various test solutions and take them to your table. Keep the frog nerve preparation moist with Ringer's solution during the entire experiment. Prepare the frog by cutting the skin away from the hip (see figure 23.1). Do not cut, pinch, or otherwise damage the sciatic nerve on the posterior side of the thigh.

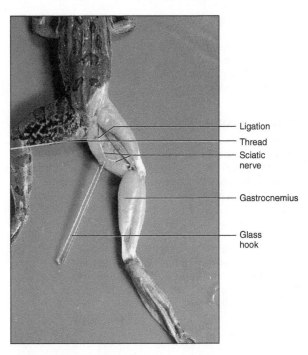

FIGURE 23.1 **Ligation of the Sciatic Nerve of the Frog**

Gently remove the nerve from between the muscles with a glass rod (see figure 23.1). Do not stretch the nerve; leave it intact alongside the muscles. You can attach the gastrocnemius to a myograph transducer, as you did in Exercise 19, or just examine the muscle for a response.

Nerve Response to Physical Stimuli

Flush the nerve with Ringer's solution and make sure it remains moist. Nerve stimulation can be determined by the corresponding muscular contraction. You measure the effects of the nerve stimulation by the contraction of the gastrocnemius muscle. If the nerve is stimulated, then the gastrocnemius muscle should contract.

Cut a small (10 cm) section of cotton thread and gently slip it under the sciatic nerve with a pair of fine forceps. Gently move the thread up toward the hip. When you reach the proximal location where the nerve descends into the muscle, tie off the nerve with thread and examine the effects. Loop the thread and ligate (tie off) the nerve close to the sacrum (see figure 23.1) while watching the gastrocnemius muscle.

As the thread begins to tighten on the nerve, record the response in the space provided and in the Chapter Summary Data section.

? Response of the nerve to physical stimulation:

_____ 9

After you have ligated the nerve, cut it from the anterior side, leaving the nerve attached to the gastrocnemius muscle. Moisten the nerve with Ringer's solution and prepare for the next experiment.

Nerve Response to Electrical Stimuli

Place a stimulator probe connected to a stimulator underneath the sciatic nerve, lifting the nerve away from the gastrocnemius muscle. Keep the nerve moist as you determine the minimum voltage **(threshold voltage)** required for nerve conduction. Set the stimulator to a frequency of two pulses per second and a duration of 10 milliseconds. The voltage should be set at zero (with the knob on 0.1 volt). Slowly increase the voltage until you observe the gastrocnemius twitch. As soon as you see the gastrocnemius twitch at the *lowest voltage,* record this as threshold voltage in the space provided. Turn the voltage to zero, flush the nerve with Ringer's solution, and let it rest for a moment.

? Threshold voltage: _____ 10

Continue to increase the voltage until the muscle contracts maximally. Record this as the **maximum recruitment voltage.** This voltage is obtained when all the axons of a particular nerve are stimulated.

? Maximum recruitment voltage: _____ 11

Nerve Response to Chemical Stimuli

In the following two experiments you test the response of the nerve to different chemical agents. Make sure you observe the nerve as soon as you apply the solution and rinse it as soon as the observation is made.

Acid Solution   Apply a 0.1% hydrochloric acid solution to a cotton applicator stick and gently touch the applicator to the nerve. Record the nerve response.

? Response to hydrochloric acid: _____ 12

Flush the nerve with Ringer's solution and let it rest for a moment.

Salt Solution   Gently apply a 5% sodium chloride solution to the nerve with a new cotton applicator stick. Record the response. Flush the nerve with Ringer's solution and let it rest for a moment.

? Response to sodium chloride solution: _____ 13

Nerve Response to Anesthetics

Apply a solution of **procaine hydrochloride** (Novocain) to the nerve by soaking a small square of gauze or cotton with procaine solution and placing it on the nerve for a moment. As the gauze remains on the nerve, set up the stimulator apparatus and place the nerve over the stimulator probes. Remove the gauze and stimulate the nerve with a single pulse stimulus at the voltage that produced a maximum recruitment voltage in the previous experiment. If the nerve responds to the stimulus, leave the procaine hydrochloride on longer. When the nerve does not respond, remove the gauze, flush with frog Ringer's solution, and stimulate the nerve once every 30 seconds until it recovers from the local anesthetic. Keep the nerve moist at all times with frog Ringer's solution. Record the recovery time.

? Recovery time: _____ 14

Nerve Response to Changes in Temperature

Gently touch the nerve with a glass rod at room temperature. Record the response.

? Response to gentle touch: _____ 15

Place the glass rod in an ice bath. As it equilibrates in the ice water place a small chip of ice on the nerve and let it stay there for a moment. Gently touch the nerve with the cold rod and record the response. Flush the nerve with Ringer's solution and let it rest for a moment.

? Response to gentle touch with cold stimulation:
_____ 16

Take another glass rod in a hot pad or mitts and heat one end of it in a Bunsen burner. Touch the nerve with the hot end of the glass rod. What is the response? Record your result.

? Response to gentle touch with hot stimulation:
_____ 17

Clean Up Make sure you clean your station before continuing. Place the specimen in the appropriate container, and use care when cleaning sharp instruments, such as scalpels or razor blades.

Reflexes

A reflex is a motor response to a stimulus without conscious thought. There are reflexes that pass through the spinal cord, known as **spinal reflexes,** and those that pass through the brain, known as **cranial reflexes.** The patellar reflex is a spinal reflex, while blinking in response to dust in the eye is a cranial reflex. Reflexes are involuntary, predictable responses to stimuli. Reflexes occur through **reflex arcs,** and these arcs have the following structure:

1. **Receptor** (structure that receives the stimulus and converts it to an action potential)
2. **Afferent** (sensory) **neuron** (the neuron taking the stimulus to the CNS)
3. **Integrating center** (brain or spinal cord)
4. **Efferent** (motor) **neuron** (the neuron taking the response from the CNS)
5. **Effector** (the structure causing an effect)

If the effector is skeletal muscle, it is a **somatic reflex.** If the effector is a gland, smooth muscle, or cardiac muscle, it is a **visceral,** or **autonomic, reflex.**

Most reflexes involve many neurons with many synapses and are called **polysynaptic reflex arcs.** A few reflexes involve only two neurons—a sensory neuron and a motor neuron with one synapse between them. These are **monosynaptic reflex arcs.** They are illustrated in figure 23.2.

Reflexes depend on a **stimulus,** or environmental cue; a **receptor** sensitive to the stimulus; an **afferent neuron** (or sensory neuron); an **efferent neuron** (or motor neuron); and an **effector.** The polysynaptic reflex has these structures as well as an **association neuron,** or **interneuron,** located between the afferent and efferent neurons. Interneurons take information to the brain via ascending tracts of the spinal cord.

Testing for reflexes is important for clinical evaluation of the condition of the nervous system. Decreased response or exaggerated response to a stimulus may indicate disease or damage to the nervous system. In this experiment you test several reflexes and determine if the response is **normal** (movement of an inch or two), **hyporeflexic** (showing less than average response), or **hyperreflexic** (showing an exaggerated response). If there is hyperreflexia this might indicate central nervous system damage. No reflex may indicate spinal cord damage, and hyporeflexia may be indicative of hypothyroidism.

Stretch Reflexes

For stretch reflexes, receptors are in the **muscle spindle** (figure 23.3). There are many types of nerve fibers in a muscle spindle. When a muscle is stretched, many muscle spindles are stimulated, and **primary afferent fibers** send strong signals to the spinal cord, resulting in contraction of the muscle that was stretched. This dampens the effect of stretching the muscle. Alpha motor neurons innervate the main muscle tissue and are primarily responsible for muscle contraction, while gamma motor neurons innervate the muscle spindle and regulate the sensitivity of the spindle. These allow you to make changes in the contraction of muscle such as those required when trying to maintain your balance.

Stretching the muscle causes an increase in action potentials in the sensory neuron. The impulse travels to the motor neuron, causing contraction of the muscle that is stretched. A typical example of a stretch reflex is the patellar reflex, in which striking the patellar ligament stretches the quadriceps muscles. Sensory neurons transmit this information to the spinal column, where motor neurons stimulate the quadriceps muscle to contract, thus extending the leg.

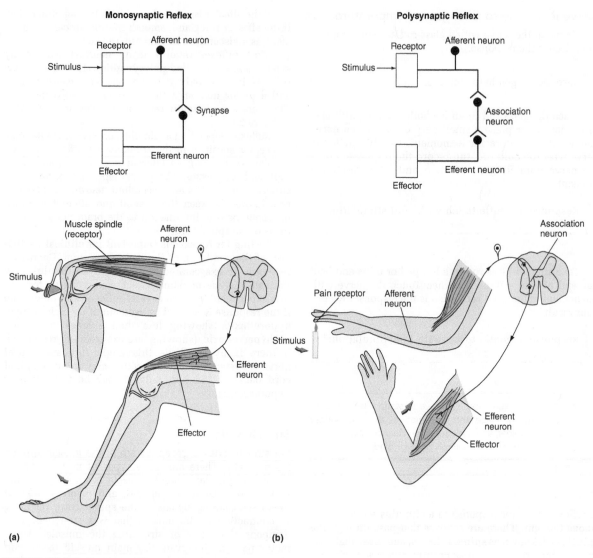

FIGURE 23.2 Reflex Arcs (a) Monosynaptic; (b) polysynaptic.

Patellar Reflex

The **patellar reflex** is a stretch reflex that tests the femoral nerve. Sensory neurons in the quadriceps muscle are stimulated by rapid lengthening of the muscle and conduct nerve impulses to the spinal cord. Sensory neurons synapse with motor neurons that innervate muscles, stimulating them to resist the stretch. It is the most frequent reflex test performed in clinical settings. Sit on the lab table with your leg hanging over the edge and have your lab partner tap you on the patellar tendon with a patellar reflex hammer. The percussion should be placed about 3 to 4 cm below the inferior edge of the patella, and it should be firm but not hard enough to hurt. Look for extension of the leg as a response to the patellar reflex (see figure 23.4).

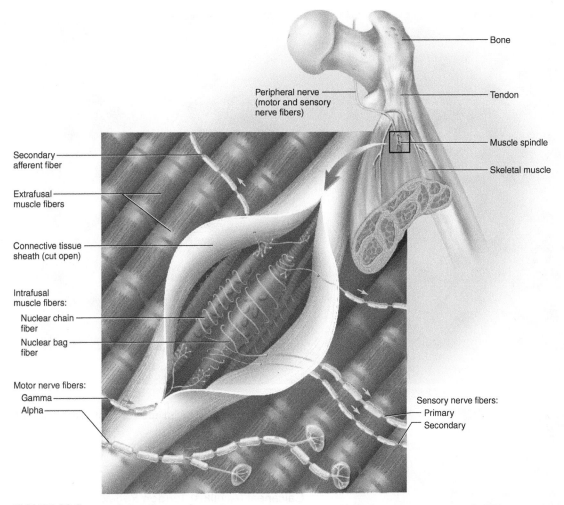

FIGURE 23.3 A Muscle Spindle

The tap stimulates the stretch receptors in the muscle and is representative of a monosynaptic reflex. Record the degree (hyperreflexic, normal, hyporeflexic) of the response.

? Patellar reflex: _____ 18

Triceps Brachii Reflex

The **triceps brachii reflex** tests the radial nerve. Sit on a chair or lie down on your back on a clean lab table or cot and place your forearm on your abdomen. Have your lab partner tap the distal tendon of the triceps brachii muscle about 2 inches proximal to the olecranon process. Look for the triceps muscle to twitch (see figure 23.5). Record your result.

? Triceps brachii reflex: _____ 19

Biceps Brachii Reflex

The **biceps brachii reflex** tests the musculocutaneous nerve. Sit comfortably and have your lab partner place his or her fingers on the biceps tendon just proximal to the antecubital fossa (see figure 23.6).

Your lab partner should tap his or her fingers with the reflex hammer, while they remain on the tendon, and

FIGURE 23.4 **Patellar Reflex**

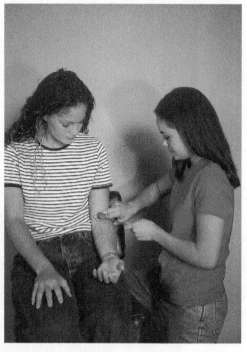

FIGURE 23.6 **Biceps Brachii Reflex**

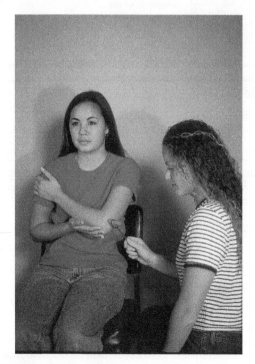

FIGURE 23.5 **Triceps Reflex**

look for the biceps brachii muscle contraction. Record your results.

? Biceps brachii reflex: _____ 20

Calcaneal (Achilles) Tendon Reflex

To test the **calcaneal tendon reflex** kneel on a chair with your foot dangling over the edge (see figure 23.7). Have your lab partner tap the calcaneal tendon to test the tibial nerve.

As your lab partner taps your calcaneal tendon, look for plantar flexion of the foot. You may see an initial movement of the foot due to the depression of the tendon by the reflex hammer, but there should be a slight pause and then another quick movement of the foot. Record your results.

? Calcaneal tendon reflex: _____ 21

Eye Reflexes

The automatic blinking of the eye is a cranial reflex and is important to keep material, such as dust, away from the outer layer of the eye, the cornea. In the first part of this experiment have your lab partner try to make you blink

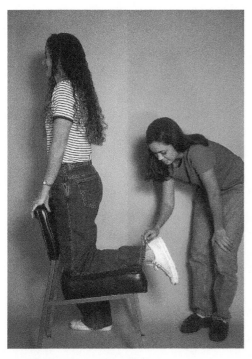

FIGURE 23.7 **Calcaneal Tendon Reflex**

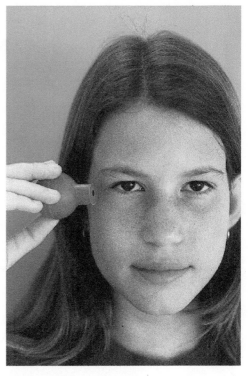

FIGURE 23.8 **Corneal Reflex**

by flicking his or her fingers near your eyes. They should not come close enough to touch your eyes. Can you prevent the blinking response? Record your answer.

 Control of blink reflex: _____ 22

Now have your lab partner take a *clean* rubber squeeze bulb (a large pipette bulb works well) and squirt a sharp blast of air across the surface of the eye (see figure 23.8).

Caution!   Use either new bulbs or ones free of debris to avoid damage to the eye.

Can you inhibit this response? Record your response.

? Control of corneal reflex: _____ 23

Plantar Response, or Babinski Reflex

Using the *metal end* of the patellar hammer, stroke the foot from the heel along the lateral, inferior surface and then toward the ball of the foot (see figure 23.9). The pressure should be firm but not uncomfortable.

Stroking the plantar surface normally results in flexion of the toes in adults. Damage to pyramidal tracts causes extension of the big toe (known as the Babinski reflex). This is important for determining spinal damage. Adults normally do not show a Babinski reflex, and the normal response in adults is to flex the foot and toes. The plantar response, or Babinski reflex, occurs in newborns and is normal. It is seen when the extension of the big toe or the fanning of the toes occurs when the plantar surface of the foot is stroked. Once myelination of the nerves occurs, the Babinski reflex disappears and is not normally found in the adult. Babinski responses in the adult are indicative of CNS problems.

FIGURE 23.9 **Babinski Reflex**

Notes

EXERCISE

23

REVIEW SECTION ▦ connect

|ANATOMY & PHYSIOLOGY

Nervous System Physiology— Stimuli and Reflexes

Name _____ Date _____

Lab Section _____ Time _____

Review Questions

1. What structure receives stimuli from the external environment and relays that stimuli to the afferent neuron?

2. What is another name for an efferent neuron?

3. What is a reflex?

4. What kind of reflex has only two neurons?

5. Polysynaptic reflexes have a neuron specific to them. What is the name of that neuron?

6. In numbers of synapses, what kind of reflex is a patellar reflex?

7. After patients leave the operating room they are transferred to an area called the "recovery room." Correlate the meaning of the word *recovery* in this context with what you have learned about the recovery of nerves in this exercise.

8. Draw a monosynaptic reflex arc in the space provided. Label your illustration using the terms provided.

   receptor

   motor neuron

   effector

   sensory neuron

   synapse

9. What action occurs with a hyperreflexic response? What action happens with a hyporeflexic response?

10. List the positive responses obtained in the frog experiment, and correlate this with the specificity of neuronal sensitivity.

11. What was the threshold voltage observed in the nerve response?

? Chapter Summary Data

Use this section to record your results from questions within the exercise.

1. _____   13. _____

2. _____   14. _____

3. _____   15. _____

4. _____   16. _____

5. _____   17. _____

6. _____   18. _____

7. _____   19. _____

8. _____   20. _____

9. _____   21. _____

10. _____   22. _____

11. _____   23. _____

12. _____

24

LABORATORY

Introduction to Sensory Receptors

INTRODUCTION

The gateway to understanding our world comes from our ability to sense the environment within our bodies and the environment around us. There are two main classes of sense—**general (somesthetic) senses** and **special senses.** General senses occur in many locations of the body and are found in places such as the skin, muscle, joints, and viscera. The senses of touch, pressure, changes in temperature, pain, blood pressure, and stretching are general senses. Special senses occur in specific locations, such as the eye, ear, tongue, and nose, and include taste, smell, sight, hearing, and balance.

Sense receptors are not uniformly distributed throughout the body. In some areas, specific sense receptors are absent, or few in number, while in other areas they are densely clustered. This pattern of uneven distribution is called **punctate distribution.**

Our perception of the environment is dependent on environmental **stimuli.** These stimuli are classified by type, or **modalities,** such as light, heat, sound, pressure, and specific chemicals. **Receptors** are the receiving units in the body that respond to an adequate stimulus. They transform the stimulus to neural signals transmitted by sensory nerves and neural tracts to the brain, which interprets the message. If any link in this sensory chain is broken, or if the stimulus is not sufficient, the perception of stimuli cannot occur.

Receptors respond to specific modalities, and each receptor can be classified according to the type of stimulus it responds to. **Photoreceptors** detect light (for example, the retina in the eye); **thermoreceptors,** located in the skin and other areas, detect changes in temperature; **proprioceptors** detect changes in the position of the body and in tension, such as those in tendons when a muscle contracts; **pain receptors,** or **nociceptors,** are present as naked nerve endings throughout much of the body; **mechanoreceptors** are receptive to mechanical stimuli (for example, touch receptors or receptors in the ear that respond to sound

or motion); **baroreceptors** respond to changes in blood pressure; and **chemoreceptors** respond to changes in the chemical environment (for example, taste and smell). These receptors are discussed in the Saladin text in chapter 16, "Sense Organs."

The skin has several types of receptors and therefore makes a good starting point for understanding sense organs. There are receptors for pressure, pain, temperature, and light touch in your skin. You may want to review the major sensory receptors in the skin, such as Meissner's corpuscles, pacinian (lamellated) corpuscles, and pain receptors in Laboratory Exercise 7 before you begin this exercise.

OBJECTIVES

At the end of this exercise you should be able to

1. define modality and receptor;
2. list the major receptor types in the body;
3. define punctate distribution of sensory receptors;
4. distinguish between tonic and phasic receptors;
5. define adaptation in reference to a stimulus;
6. distinguish between relative and absolute determination of stimuli;
7. define referred pain.

MATERIALS

Blunt metal probes

Dishpan (or large finger bowls) of ice water (2 L)

Dishpan of room temperature water

Dishpan of warm water (45° C)

Towels

Small centimeter ruler

Black, washable, fine-tipped felt markers

Red, washable, fine-tipped felt markers

328   **LABORATORY 24** Introduction to Sensory Receptors

Blue, washable, fine-tipped felt markers

Two-point discriminators (or a mechanical compass)

Three lab thermometers

Hand lotion

Von Frey hairs (horsehair glued on a wooden stick)

Tweezers

PROCEDURE

Mapping Fine-Touch Receptors

Fine-touch receptors are of two types, Meissner's corpuscles and Merkel discs. You can map these receptors by testing the ability of your lab partner to distinguish fine touch.

1. Draw a square, 2 cm on a side, with a black, washable marker on the anterior surface of the forearm. If you apply a little hand lotion to the skin before doing this test, the ink comes off more easily after the experiment.
2. Use a Von Frey hair (a stiff bristle hair attached to a matchstick) to map the number of areas in the square that can be perceived by your lab partner. Press only until the hair bends slightly to stimulate the touch corpuscles.
3. Record the location of each positive result with the marker. How many positive responses did you get in the square on the forearm? Record your result in the following space and in the Chapter Summary Data section at the end of the exercise.

? Number of anterior forearm responses: _____ 1

4. Repeat the experiment on the *posterior* surface of the *arm* using another square 2 cm on a side. How does the number of receptors here compare to those on the forearm? Record your results.

? Number of responses on posterior side of the arm:

_____ 2

Two-Point Discrimination Test

The sensitivity of touch is dependent on the number of fine-touch receptors per unit area of the skin. You can map the relative density of the receptors in the skin by performing a two-point discrimination test. The idea behind the test is to determine the *minimum distance* that your lab partner is able to recognize as two points. This is illustrated in figure 24.1.

1. Have your lab partner sit with eyes closed and his or her hand, palm up, resting on the lab counter.
2. Using the two-point discriminator (be careful as some two-point discriminators can have sharp points), or a

mechanical compass, touch your lab partner's fingertip simultaneously with both points of the instrument and see if he or she can sense one or two points. In order to establish an accurate reading make sure that you gently touch both points of the discriminator at the same time. If you touch with one point of the discriminator and then another, your lab partner may perceive two points in time and not in space.

3. A good way to establish accuracy is to occasionally touch just one of the points on your lab partner's fingertip. Another way is to vary the spread of the discriminator. You might begin with 3 cm and then adjust it to 0.5 cm followed by a 2 cm spread. Record your results.

? Minimum distance perceived as two points on

fingertip: _____ 3

4. Now move to the posterior of the arm. Establish the minimum distance that is perceived as two points by your lab partner. Record your results.

? Minimum distance perceived as two points on the

posterior arm: _____ 4

? Is there a difference between the fingertip and the

posterior arm? _____ 5

? If there is, how might the difference in distance perceived be explained in terms of the number of nerve

endings per unit area? _____ 6

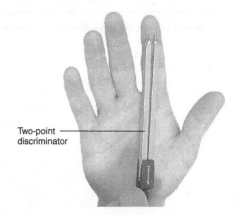

Two-point
discriminator

FIGURE 24.1 **Two-Point Discrimination**

5. Now try the palm and then the back of the shoulder or neck. Record the results.

❔ Minimum distance perceived as two points on palm:

_____ 7

❔ Minimum distance perceived as two points on back of

shoulder or neck: _____ 8

Mapping Temperature Receptors

The skin has receptors that are sensitive to cool or warm temperatures. In this part of the exercise you determine the relative numbers of these receptors.

1. Mark off a square that is 2 cm on a side on the anterior forearm of your lab partner using a washable marker.
2. Take two blunt metal probes and place the tip of one in an ice water bath and another in a warm water bath (45° C).
3. Let the probes reach the temperature of each bath, which should take a minute or two.
4. Have your lab partner close his or her eyes and rest an arm on the lab counter.
5. Remove one of the probes and quickly wipe it on a clean towel. Test the ability of your lab partner to distinguish between cool and warm by using the tip of the blunt probe on your lab partner's forearm. Systematically test areas in the square. When your lab partner perceives cold (not just touch) in a location, mark it with an "X." Retest the area with the warm probe and place an "O" in the location where warm is perceived.

❔ Number of cool receptors in the square: _____ 9

❔ Number of warm receptors in the square: _____ 10

❔ What is the ratio of "X" to "O" (cold/warm receptors)

in the square? _____ 11

Adaptation to Touch

Receptors can be classified by the length of time it takes for them to adapt to a stimulus. **Tonic receptors** continuously perceive stimuli (they do not adapt), while **phasic receptors** perceive the stimulus initially and then adapt. In this experiment you try to determine if the sense of fine touch is tonic or phasic.

1. Cut a small piece of paper, about 2 cm on a side, and crumple it into a small ball the size of a pea.
2. Have your lab partner close his or her eyes and place the hand, anterior side up, comfortably on the lab desk.
3. With a pair of tweezers, place the ball of paper on your lab partner's palm. Is the paper ball perceived after a few seconds?
4. Record your results in the following space and determine whether the sense of light touch is tonic or phasic.

❔ Results: _____ 12

Locating Stimulus with Proprioception

In this exercise you use washable markers of two colors. Location of the stimulus is dependent on both skin receptors and cerebellar function. Have your lab partner close his or her eyes and rest a forearm on the lab counter. Touch your lab partner's forearm with a felt marker and have him or her try to locate the same spot with a felt marker of another color. Test at least five locations on various parts of the forearm, and repeat each location at least twice. Now try the fingertip and palm of the hand and record the result.

❔ Maximum distance error on the forearm: _____ 13

❔ On the fingertip: _____ 14

❔ On the palm: _____ 15

Another method to test proprioreception is to close your eyes and *gently* try to touch the lateral corner of your eye with your fingertip. Have your lab partner watch you and determine the accuracy of your attempt. While your eyes are still closed, bring your hand far behind your head and then try to touch the bottom part of your earlobe or the exact tip of your chin. Record the error distance, if any, for each location.

❔ Corner of eye: _____ 16

❔ Earlobe: _____ 17

❔ Tip of chin: _____ 18

Temperature Judgment

In this exercise you examine the *adaptation* of thermoreceptors to temperature and the ability to determine temperature by **absolute value** or by **relative value.**

330   **LABORATORY 24**   Introduction to Sensory Receptors

On the lab counter locate three dishpans or large finger bowls full of water. One bowl, located on the right, should be marked "Cold" (it should be about 10° C); another bowl, located on the left, should be marked "Warm" (it should be about 40–45° C); and the middle bowl should be marked "Room Temperature." Place one hand in the cold dish and the other in the warm dish and let them adjust to the temperature for a few minutes. If your hand begins to ache in the cold water, you may remove it for a short time, but try to keep it in the cold water for as long as possible during the adjustment time. After your hands have equilibrated, place them both in the room temperature water and describe to your lab partner the temperature (cold, warm, hot) of the water as sensed by each hand. How does the hand that was in cold water feel in the room temperature water, and how does the hand that was in warm water feel in the room temperature water? Record your results.

? Cold hand perception: _____ 19

? Warm hand perception: _____ 20

If the determination of temperature is absolute, the room temperature water should feel the same whether you are testing it with your cold hand or your warm hand. If it is relative, the room temperature water should feel warmer with your cold hand and colder with your warm hand.

? Is the determination of the temperature of water

absolute or relative: _____ 21

? How did your experiment prove this? _____ 22

Referred Pain

Referred pain is the perception of pain in one area of the body when the pain is somewhere else. An example of

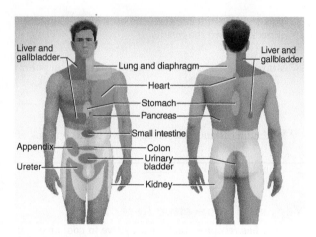

FIGURE 24.2 **Referred Pain**

referred pain is the pain felt in the left shoulder and arm when a person is suffering from a heart attack or chest pain (angina pectoris) (see figure 24.2).

Frequently, neural impulses have convergent pathways where nerves receiving stimuli from the skin or muscle in one area follow the same general ascending tract that sensory information from an organ (such as the kidney or gallbladder) do. If there are pain stimuli in that organ, an individual may feel the pain in the skin that shares the tract.

Place your elbow into a dish of ice water and leave it there for 2 painful minutes. Describe the sensation you feel and the location of the sensation. Record your results.

? Description of sensation: _____ 23

? Initial location of sensation: _____ 24

? Sensation after 2-minute period: _____ 25

REVIEW SECTION ▦ **connect**
|ANATOMY & PHYSIOLOGY

Introduction to Sensory Receptors

Name _____ Date _____

Lab Section _____ Time _____

Review Questions

1. An area with a great number of fine touch receptors is the upper lip. What can you predict about the ability of the upper lip to distinguish two points?

2. Cool receptors in the skin are activated between 12° and 35° C. Warm receptors are activated between 25° and 45° C. When the temperature is below 12° C or above 45° C, pain receptors in the skin are activated. You or your lab partner may have had an experience with very cold conditions, such as when cleaning out a freezer or holding dry ice. What perception is sensed?

3. Adaptation is important to sensory stimulation. We are bombarded with stimuli during most of the day, and much of what we sense is filtered from conscious thought. How is adaptation used by pickpockets?

4. In terms of receptor density, describe why it is difficult to find the same location on the forearm when your eyes are closed.

5. In regard to sense organs, what is punctate distribution?

6. In reference to the sense organs, what is a modality?

7. What types of receptors are sensitive to the following modalities?

   a. light   d. sound

   b. touch   e. smell

   c. temperature

8. What type of receptor is responsive to extremely hot sensations?

9. Meissner's corpuscles respond to what type of sensation?

10. What type of receptor determines the weight of an object when you pick it up?

11. Which type of receptor (tonic/phasic) adapts to light in a darkened movie theater?

12. When you drink a burning hot liquid, the "chest pain" felt in the region of the sternum does not really occur there. What is this type of pain called?

? Chapter Summary Data

Use this section to record your results from questions within the exercise.

1. _____   14. _____

2. _____   15. _____

3. _____   16. _____

4. _____   17. _____

5. _____   18. _____

6. _____   19. _____

7. _____   20. _____

8. _____   21. _____

9. _____   22. _____

10. _____   23. _____

11. _____   24. _____

12. _____   25. _____

13. _____

LABORATORY

Taste and Smell

INTRODUCTION

Like most of our senses, we take for granted our senses of taste and smell. They are not fully appreciated unless they are lost. People who have lost the sense of smell find food difficult to eat, since they derive little or no pleasure from the act of eating. In this exercise you examine the structure and function of the organs involved in these two important senses.

Both taste and smell are examples of **chemoreception,** in which specific chemical compounds are detected by the sense organs and interpreted by various regions of the brain. The sense of taste and the sense of olfaction are covered in the Saladin text in chapter 16, "Sense Organs."

OBJECTIVES

At the end of this exercise you should be able to

1. list the two major chemoreceptors located in the region of the head;
2. diagram a taste bud;
3. trace the sense of smell from the nose to the integrative areas of the brain;
4. trace the sense of taste from the tongue to the integrative areas of the brain;
5. list the five tastes perceived by humans;
6. describe what happens in an olfactory reflex;
7. compare and contrast the senses of taste and smell.

MATERIALS

Sterile cotton-tipped applicators

Five dropper bottles containing one of the following:

    Solution of salt water (3%) labeled "Salty"

    Quinine solution (tonic water) labeled "Bitter"

    Vinegar solution (household vinegar or 5% acetic acid solution) labeled "Acidic"

    Sugar solution (3% sucrose) labeled "Sweet"

    Umami solution (15 g MSG in 500 mL water) labeled "Umami"

Biohazard bag

Prepared slides of taste buds

Microscopes

Roll of household paper towels

Small bowl of salt crystals (household salt)

Small bowl of sugar crystals (household granulated sugar)

Flat toothpicks

Small bottle (100 mL) of household ammonia

Several small vials (10–20 mL) screw-cap bottles with essential oil labeled "Peppermint," "Almond," "Wintergreen," and "Camphor" (keep vials in separate wide-mouthed jars to prevent cross-contamination of scents)

Four small vials colored red and labeled "Wild Cherry" filled with benzaldehyde solution

Four small vials of "Almond" essence

One vial of dilute perfume (one part perfume, five parts ethyl alcohol)

Marking pens

Noseclips and alcohol swabs

Selection of four or five fruit nectars (such as Kern's nectars), two cans each: apricot, coconut/pineapple, strawberry, mango, peach, apple

Small, 3 oz paper cups (89 mL), five per student (or student pair)

Napkins

PROCEDURE

Examination of Taste Buds

Examine the prepared slide of taste buds and compare them to figure 25.1. The taste buds are located on the sides of papillae on the tongue. The taste buds appear lighter than the surrounding tissue (like microscopic onions cut in long sections). Taste buds consist of **supporting cells** and **taste cells,** specialized epithelial cells, with hairs that project into the **taste pores** near the surface of the tongue. The basal portion of the taste cell synapses with sensory neurons.

Transmission of Sense of Gustation to the Brain

The sense of taste, or **gustation,** is picked up by the receptors in taste buds primarily in the tongue, although there are also receptors in the soft palate and pharynx. The sense of taste travels through the facial nerves, glossopharyngeal nerves, and vagus nerves to the medulla oblongata. From there, some fibers travel to either the hypothalamus or amygdala where autonomic reflexes (such as swallowing) occur. Other fibers travel to the thalamus and then to higher brain centers, such as the postcentral gyrus, where the sense of taste is determined. From the postcentral gyrus, fibers take neural impulses to the orbitofrontal cortex, where sight and smell are integrated with taste. The sense of taste is influenced by a food's smell, appearance, temperature, and texture, even the mood of the individual.

Taste Determination of Solid Materials

Gustatory receptors are stimulated by specific chemicals in solution. Fluid runs down the sides of the tongue papillae, where the hair cells of the receptors are located. Blot your tongue thoroughly with a paper towel. Make sure the surface is relatively dry. Have your lab partner select either the sugar crystals or the salt crystals and place a small scoop (with the end of a flat toothpick) on your tongue. Keep your mouth open and do not swirl saliva around. Can you determine what the sample is?

Now close your mouth and see if you can determine the nature of the sample.

Mapping the Tongue for Taste Receptors

In this section you determine if receptors for taste are distributed evenly over the tongue or are located in specialized areas. There are five primary tastes: sweet, sour, salty, bitter, and umami. Umami gives meat and cheese their tastes, and it can be referred to as the taste of "savory." We have varying degrees of sensitivity to these five tastes. Some of us find bitter tastes to be especially objectionable, while others do not seem to mind them as much. As you perform the taste experiments determine if members of your class are equally sensitive to the same

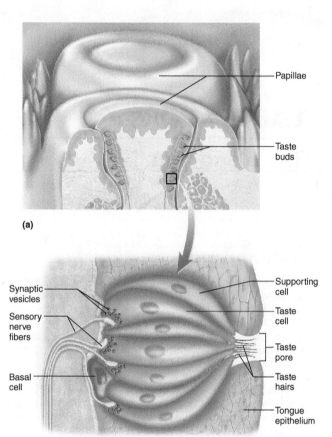

(a)

(b)

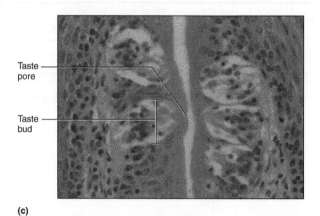

(c)

FIGURE 25.1 **Taste Buds** (a) Taste buds on sides of a tongue papilla; (b) details of taste buds; (c) photomicrograph (100x).

tastes as you are. If you have food allergies you may wish to omit this part of the lab. People with allergies, migraines, or heart problems should avoid the tasting of umami, the taste of glutamate.

Select one of the dropper bottles labeled "Sweet," "Sour," "Salty," "Bitter," or "Umami." Using a sterile cotton-tipped applicator stick, apply one of the tasting solutions to the cotton tip. Saturate the cotton tip. Remember to keep track of the substance on your applicator stick. *Do not* reuse the applicator sticks. Dab the entire surface of your lab partner's tongue and determine by nod or hand signals when perception of the taste occurs. *Do not* have your lab partner tell you about the taste at first, because the movement of the tongue will wash the solution to other areas of the tongue and you may get a false reading. You should test the front, lower sides, middle, and back of the tongue. Map the result of your taste test in figure 25.2. Certain regions of the tongue are more sensitive to a specific taste and these are variable among individuals. Throw the applicator stick in the biohazard bag. Repeat the test with a *new applicator stick* for each of the five solutions. *Do not contaminate* the solutions by reusing the applicator stick with the same or different solutions after it has been in your lab partner's mouth!

Transmission of Sense of Olfaction to Brain

Examine a model, chart, or diagram of an inferior view of the brain and locate the olfactory nerves, olfactory bulb, and olfactory tract. The sense of smell begins in the nose, where **olfactory cells** (specialized neurons) receive chemical input from the environment. These neurons are clustered in bundles that make up the **olfactory nerve** and they pass from the nasal mucosa to the **olfactory bulb** at the base of the frontal lobe (see figure 25.3). Some fibers travel to the temporal lobe, where the perception of smell occurs, while others travel to the hippocampus or amygdala, where the memory of smell is stored or the emotional response of smell occurs.

Olfactory Reflex

Take a small bottle of household ammonia and place it under the nose of your lab partner. Have your lab partner take a brief sniff from the bottle. If there is a visible movement of the head in a posterior direction then your lab partner demonstrates an olfactory reflex to smell. Record the results of your experiment below.

Olfactory reflex:

? _____ 1a yes

? _____ 1b no

? What might be the adaptive benefit for people having

an olfactory reflex? _____ 2

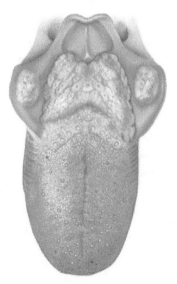

FIGURE 25.2 **Map the Taste Receptors You Determine by Experiment Here**

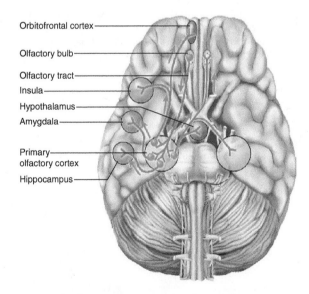

Orbitofrontal cortex

Olfactory bulb

Olfactory tract

Insula

Hypothalamus

Amygdala

Primary olfactory cortex

Hippocampus

FIGURE 25.3 **The Transmission of Olfaction from the Olfactory Bulbs to the Brain**

Visual Cues in Smell Interpretation

In this section you examine the influence of visual cues on the interpretation of smell. You will seek to determine whether the color of a substance has any effect on what you perceive the smell to be. Have your lab partner show you a small vial labeled "Almond" and then smell it. Now examine and smell the small red vial labeled "Wild Cherry." Do you perceive these as two separate smells? Close your eyes and have your lab partner select a vial for you. Can you tell which one it is?

Olfactory Discrimination

Obtain four vials of different scents—peppermint, almond, wintergreen, and camphor. While keeping your eyes closed try to determine the name of each essential oil as your lab partner presents it to you. Record how many of the smells you got correct out of the four. If you are hypersensitive to smells, have your lab partner do this section of the experiment.

? Number correct: _____ 3

Adaptation to Smell

Adaptation to smell by the olfactory receptors occurs very rapidly, but the adaptation by the receptors is incomplete. Complete adaptation to smell probably occurs by additional CNS inhibition of the olfactory signals. In this section of the experiment you are trying to determine approximately how long olfactory adaptation takes. Close your eyes and plug one nostril. Inhale the scent from a vial of dilute perfume or one of the scents from the olfactory discrimination test, until the smell decreases significantly. Have your lab partner record the time when you begin the experiment and how long it takes for the perception of smell to decrease significantly. How long does this take?

? Length of time for significant reduction of the smell:

_____ 4

? What might be the evolutionary advantage of

adaptation to smell? _____ 5

Predict whether adaptation to one smell causes adaptation to another smell. Record your prediction that the smell of one material does or does not cause adaptation to another smell.

Now smell the wintergreen or peppermint vial. Does the adaptation of one smell cause the olfactory receptors to adapt to other smells?

Taste and Olfaction Tests

This experiment demonstrates the dependence of the sense of smell as a component of what we call *taste*. Obtain four or five small cups (3 oz) and, using a marking pen, label each with the name of the fruit juice or nectar it will contain. Have your lab partner select several types of fruit nectars and pour each into the proper cup.

Caution! If you have a particular food allergy notify your instructor. You may wish to omit part or all of this test.

Sit with your eyes and your nose closed (use noseclips or pinch off your nostrils with your finger and thumb) and try to determine the sample presented to you by your lab partner. Your lab partner should place the sample cup (sample unknown to you) in your hand and you should guess what fruit nectar is in the cup. After you have "tasted" the sample try to name it. Test all the samples with your nose closed. After you make your determination release your nostrils but still keep your eyes closed and taste the samples again. Record the results. How accurate is your comparison?

Trial Number	Sample	Accuracy or Detection (Yes/No)	
		Nose Closed	Nose Open
1	Apricot		
2	Mango		
3	Coconut/pineapple		
4	Strawberry		
5	Peach		
6	Other		

REVIEW SECTION ▦ connect
|ANATOMY & PHYSIOLOGY

Taste and Smell

Name _____ Date _____

Lab Section _____ Time _____

Review Questions

1. Why does material have to be in solution for it to be sensed as taste?

2. What are the primary tastes?

3. Did everyone in your lab have the same sensitivity to taste, such as sweet, sour, or bitter?

4. Describe the pathway of smell from the olfactory receptors to the temporal lobes of the brain.

5. What structures are involved in taking the sense of taste from the taste buds to the brain?

6. Where are the taste buds located?

7. What is the exact region of the nasal cavity receptive to smell stimuli?

8. Can you determine the evolutionary advantage for having taste buds that determine unpleasant bitter compounds in many plant species?

9. Some individuals with severe sinus infections can lose their sense of smell. How can an infection that spreads from the frontal or maxillary sinus impair the sense of smell? What structure or structures might be affected?

338   **REVIEW 25**   Taste and Smell

10. Material must be in solution for it to be perceived by gustatory receptors. What process is used (olfaction, gustation) to perceive a lipid-based food, such as garlic or peppermint?

11. Some smells that we perceive as two separate smells are actually identical. What are the other cues that we use to distinguish these two "smells" as being distinct?

12. How does a cold (rhinovirus) influence our perception of the flavor of food?

13. Does adaptation to one smell influence the adaptation to another smell?

14. Compare your "taste map" of your tongue to the one from your lab partner. Are they exact? Did you have differences in sensitivity to specific tastes?

? Chapter Summary Data

Use this section to record your results from questions within the exercise.

1a. _____

1b. _____

2. _____

3. _____

4. _____

5. _____

LABORATORY

Eye and Vision

INTRODUCTION

In most people eyesight accounts for much of our accumulated knowledge. The importance of the eye can be inferred in that 4 of the 12 cranial nerves are dedicated, at least in part, to either receiving visual stimuli or coordinating the movement of the eyes. The anatomy and physiology of the eye are discussed in the Saladin text in chapter 16, "Sense Organs."

Anatomically, the eye consists of an anterior portion, visible as we look at the face of an individual, and a posterior portion, situated in the orbit of the skull. Light from the external environment travels through a number of transparent structures that bend and focus the light on the retina, the receptive layer of the eye that converts light energy to nerve impulses. Nerve impulses travel from the eyes to the optic nerves to the occipital lobes of the brain, where they are interpreted as sight. This exercise involves learning the structure of the eye and correlating those structures to the function of vision by performing basic physiology experiments.

OBJECTIVES

At the end of this exercise you should be able to

1. identify the major structures of the mammalian eye;
2. describe the six extrinsic muscles of the eye and their effect on the movement of the eye;
3. distinguish between the pupil and the iris of the eye;
4. describe the position of the choroid in reference to the retina and the sclera;
5. describe the function of the rods and the cones of the eye;
6. define the near point of the eye;
7. determine the visual field for both eyes;
8. demonstrate the Snellen vision tests and those for accommodation and astigmatism.

MATERIALS

Models and charts of the eye

Snellen charts

Astigmatism charts

Vision Disk (Hubbard) or large protractor

Microscopes

Prepared microscope slides of eye in sagittal section

Preserved sheep or cow eyes

Dissection trays

Dissection gloves (latex or plastic)

Scalpel or razor blades

Animal waste disposal container

Card with fine print (8-point font)

3-by-5-inch cards

Ishihara color book or colored yarn

Ruler (approximately 35 cm)

Ophthalmoscope and batteries

Penlight

Desk lamp with 60-watt bulb

Paper card with a simple colored image (red circle, blue triangle) printed on it

PROCEDURE

External Features of the Eye

The external anatomy of the eye and the accessory structures are illustrated in figure 26.1. Examine the eye of your lab partner and compare it to the figure. The **pupil** is located in the center of the eye and is surrounded by the colored **iris**. The **sclera** is the white of the eye, and it is

340 **LABORATORY 26** Eye and Vision

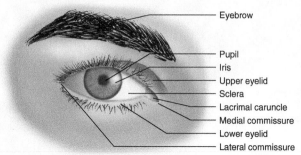

FIGURE 26.1 **External Anatomy of the Eye**

- Eyebrow
- Pupil
- Iris
- Upper eyelid
- Sclera
- Lacrimal caruncle
- Medial commissure
- Lower eyelid
- Lateral commissure

The eyelids join together at the **lateral commissure** and the **medial commissure.** There is a small piece of tissue near the medial commissure known as the **lacrimal caruncle.** Examine the **upper eyelid** and **eyelashes** and the **lower eyelid** and eyelashes, which prevent material from entering the eyes and (in the case of the eyelids) reduce visual stimulation when we sleep. Look also at the **eyebrow** located on the supraorbital ridge.

The sclera is a protective portion of the eye that is an attachment point for the muscles of the eye and helps maintain the intraocular pressure (the pressure inside the eye). The pressure maintains the shape of the eye and keeps the retina adhered to the back wall of the eye. The sclera is continuous with the transparent cornea in the front of the eye.

Attached to the sclera are the **extrinsic muscles** of the eye. There are six extrinsic muscles, which, in coordination, move the eye in quick and precise ways. Locate these muscles on a model and compare them to figure 26.2.

covered by a membrane, known as the **conjunctiva**, which continues underneath the eyelids. Numerous blood vessels traverse the conjunctiva, and if they become dilated anteriorly they give the eye the appearance of being "bloodshot."

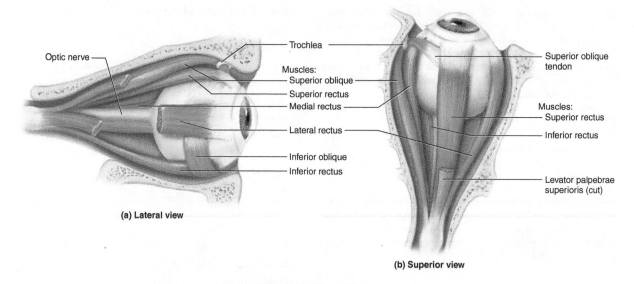

- Optic nerve
- Trochlea
- Muscles:
  - Superior oblique
  - Superior rectus
  - Medial rectus
- Lateral rectus
- Inferior oblique
- Inferior rectus

(a) Lateral view

- Superior oblique tendon
- Muscles:
  - Superior rectus
  - Inferior rectus
- Levator palpebrae superioris (cut)

(b) Superior view

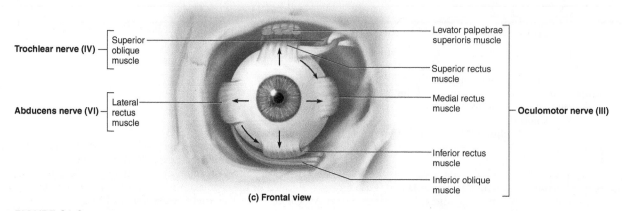

- **Trochlear nerve (IV)** — Superior oblique muscle
- **Abducens nerve (VI)** — Lateral rectus muscle
- Levator palpebrae superioris muscle
- Superior rectus muscle
- Medial rectus muscle
- Inferior rectus muscle
- Inferior oblique muscle
- **Oculomotor nerve (III)**

(c) Frontal view

FIGURE 26.2 **Right Eye, External Features**

TABLE 26.1	Extrinsic Muscles of the Eye	
Muscle Name	**Innervation**	**Direction Eye Turns**
Lateral rectus	VI (abducens)	Laterally
Medial rectus	III (oculomotor)	Medially
Superior rectus	III (oculomotor)	Superiorly
Inferior rectus	III (oculomotor)	Inferiorly
Inferior oblique	III (oculomotor)	Superiorly and laterally
Superior oblique	IV (trochlear)	Inferiorly and laterally

These muscles and their action on the eye are listed in table 26.1.

A structure important in the maintenance of the exterior of the eye is the **lacrimal apparatus.** This consists of the **lacrimal gland** located superior and lateral to the eye (see figure 26.3). Tears bathe and protect the eye and clean dust from its surface. The fluid drains through the **nasolacrimal duct** into the nasal cavity.

Interior of the Eye

From the anterior of the eye, the first layer covering the inside of the eyelid and extending across the sclera is the conjunctiva. The conjunctiva is composed of epithelial tissue and is an important indicator of a number of clinical conditions (for example, conjunctivitis). In the center of the

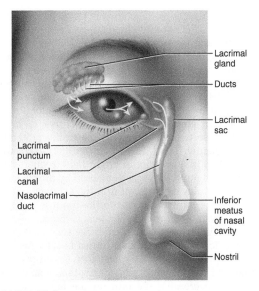

FIGURE 26.3 Lacrimal Apparatus

eye is the transparent **cornea** (see figure 26.4). The cornea is the structure of the eye most responsible for the bending of light rays that strike the eye. The lens adjusts the images in order to focus. It is composed of dense connective tissue and is avascular. Why would the presence of blood vessels in the cornea be a visual liability?

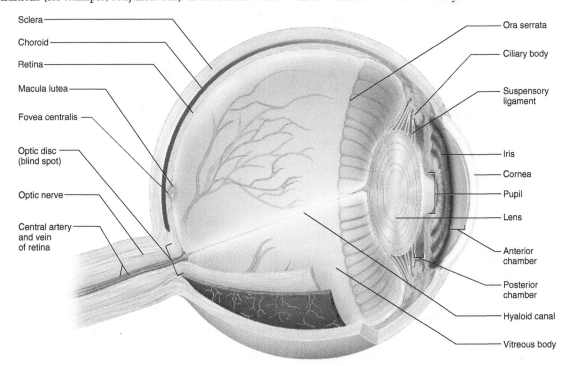

FIGURE 26.4 Sagittal Section of the Eye

Directly posterior to the cornea is the **anterior cavity,** subdivided into the **anterior chamber,** between the cornea and the **iris,** and the **posterior chamber,** between the iris and the **lens.** The anterior cavity is filled with **aqueous humor,** produced by the **ciliary body.** Only a few milliliters of aqueous humor are produced each day, and this amount is absorbed by a **venous sinus** (canal of Schlemm).

The iris is what gives us a particular eye color. People with blue and gray eyes are more sensitive to bright light than those with brown eyes, due to the protective pigment melanin found in brown eyes. The **circular muscles** of the iris constrict in bright light, reducing the diameter of the **pupil** (the space enclosed by the iris), and the **radial muscles** constrict in dim light, increasing the diameter of the pupil. Posterior to the pupil is the lens, made of a crystalline protein. The lens is more pliable in youth and stiffens as a person ages. Because of the loss of this elasticity, people in their forties usually begin to use reading glasses. The ciliary muscle in the ciliary body contracts and the suspensory ligaments that attach to the lens loosen, decreasing the pull on the lens. The lens becomes rounder, allowing for close focusing.

Posterior to the lens is the **posterior cavity,** or **vitreous chamber** (see figure 26.4). This cavity occupies most of the posterior portion, or fundus, of the eye. The posterior cavity is filled with the **vitreous body (vitreous humor),** a clear, jellylike fluid that maintains the shape of the eyeball. The eye has three layers or **tunics.** The most superficial layer is the **fibrous layer,** and it consists of the **sclera** (white of the eye) and the **cornea** (an anterior transparent continuation of the sclera). The cornea allows light to penetrate into the interior of the eye. The middle layer of the eye is the **vascular layer** or **uvea** (YOU-vee-uh) and consists of the **choroid,** the **ciliary body,** and the **iris.** The blood vessels found in the choroid nourish the eye and the pigmentation prevents light from scattering and blurring vision. The layer closest to the **vitreous body** is the **inner layer,** and it is composed of the **retina** and the **optic nerve.** The retina consists of an outer **pigmented epithelium,** which absorbs light passing through the eye and prevents light scattering, and an inner **neural layer.**

The retina converts visible light into action potentials. **Photoreceptor cells** (the **rods** and **cones**) are sensitive to light and generate an electrochemical signal. Rods and cones synapse with **bipolar cells,** which are deep to the retina. Thus, the visual stimulation that occurs in the posterior portion of the eye is transmitted anteriorly (toward the vitreous body) to the bipolar cells. In the dark, photoreceptor cells release the neurotransmitter glutamate, which inhibits bipolar cells. When light strikes the retina, the inhibitory glutamate is not released from the photoreceptor cells, and the bipolar cells fire. The bipolar cells synapse with **ganglion cells,** and the axons of the ganglion cells comprise the **optic nerve.** From there the nerve impulse is transmitted to the lateral geniculate nucleus of the thalamus and then to the occipital region

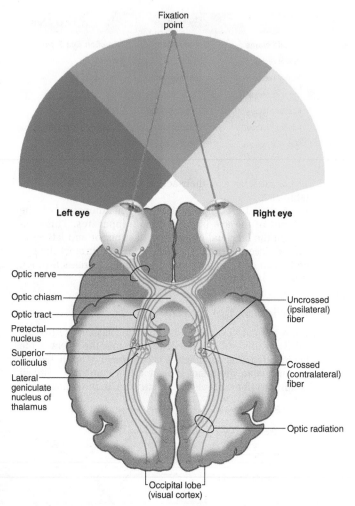

FIGURE 26.5 **Visual Pathway to the Brain**

of the brain and integrated in the temporal lobe (see figure 26.5). Images from the left visual field cross over to the right side of the brain. The right side of the brain controls motor impulses for the left side of the body. The images in the right visual field cross over to the left side of the brain.

Posterior Wall of the Eye

Obtain a microscope and a slide of the retina and compare what you see in the slide to figure 26.6. The neural layer of the retina is composed of three layers: **ganglionic, bipolar,** and **photoreceptor cells.** The photosensitive layer is composed of **rods** and **cones.** Rods are important for determining the motion and general shape of objects and for sight in dim light. They do not function for color vision. Cones are involved in color vision and in visual acuity (determining fine detail). They function in bright light.

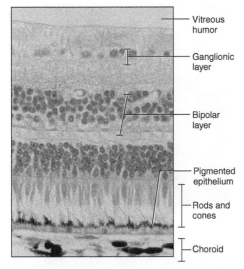

FIGURE 26.6 **Retina (400×)**

Vitreous humor

Ganglionic layer

Bipolar layer

Pigmented epithelium

Rods and cones

Choroid

Examine a model or chart of the eye and locate the **macula lutea** at the posterior region of the eye. *Macula lutea* means "yellow spot," and in the center of this structure is the **fovea centralis,** a region where the concentration of cones is greatest. In the fovea the cone cells are not covered by the neural layers as they are in the other parts of the retina. When you focus on an object intently, you are directing the image to the fovea. Locate the fovea in figure 26.7 and in models available in the lab.

Dissection of a Sheep or Cow Eye

Rinse a sheep or cow eye in running water and place it on a dissection tray. Obtain a scalpel, scissors, or new razor blade and a blunt probe. Be careful with the sharp instruments

and cut *away from* the hand holding the eye. Wear latex or plastic gloves while you perform the dissection. Carefully remove the fat and muscles from the eyeball. Using a scalpel, scissors, or razor blade, make a coronal section of the eye behind the cornea (see figure 26.8). Do not squeeze the eye with force or thrust the blade sharply because you may squirt yourself with vitreous humor. Cut through the eye entirely and note the jellylike material in the posterior cavity. This is the vitreous body. Look at the posterior portion of the eye. Note the beige retina, which may have pulled away from the darkened choroid. The choroid in humans is very dark, but you may see an iridescent color in your specimen. This is the **tapetum lucidum,** which improves night vision in some animals. The tapetum lucidum produces the "eye shine" of nocturnal animals. Also examine the tough, white sclera, which envelops the choroid.

Now examine the anterior portion of the eye. Is the lens in place? The lens in your specimen probably will not be clear due to the preserving fluid denaturing the protein of the lens. Normally, the lens is transparent and allows for light penetration.

The lens is held to the ciliary body by the suspensory ligaments (see figure 26.4). These ligaments pull on the lens and alter its shape for close or distant vision. Locate the ciliary body at the edge of the suspensory ligaments.

Turn the eye over. Is there any aqueous humor left in the anterior cavity? Make an incision through the conjunctiva and cornea into the anterior cavity. Can you determine the region of the anterior chamber and the posterior chamber that make up the anterior cavity? Locate the iris and the pupil. Dispose of the specimen in a designated waste container and rinse your dissection tools.

Visual Tracking

Eye movements are precisely controlled by the six extrinsic muscles of the eye. To determine their effectiveness, have your lab partner follow your finger as you move it

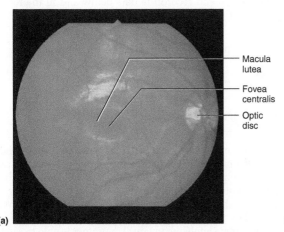

(a)

Macula lutea

Fovea centralis

Optic disc

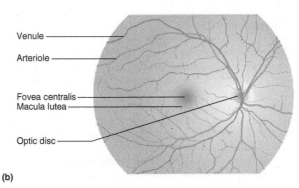

(b)

Venule

Arteriole

Fovea centralis
Macula lutea

Optic disc

FIGURE 26.7 **Eye, Posterior Surface** (a) Photograph; (b) diagram.

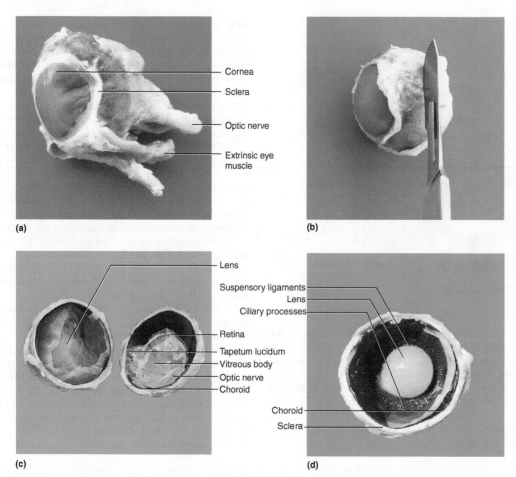

FIGURE 26.8 Dissection of a Sheep Eye (a) External features; (b) coronal section; (c) eye with vitreous body; (d) anterior eye without vitreous body.

in front of the eyes. Is the movement of the eye smooth (a normal function) or do the eyes move in a jerky fashion (an abnormal condition)? Record your results here.

Eye movement: (smooth/jerky) (select one).

Determination of the Near Point

The minimum distance an object can comfortably be held in focus is called the **near point.** The eye's ability to focus is due to the elasticity of the lens. The elasticity of the lens decreases with age. A 10-year-old is able to focus 8 to 10 cm away from the eye, yet a 65-year-old may not be able to focus closer than 80 to 100 cm. The decreased elasticity of the lens becomes noticeable around 40 to 50 years of age, when many people find reading glasses necessary because of their aging lenses. You can measure your near point by holding a paper with fine print vertically at arm's length in front of you. Close one eye and slowly move the paper closer until either you see two objects or it becomes blurry. Have your lab partner measure the distance, in

centimeters, from your eye to the paper. This is the near point distance. Measure the near point for both eyes in centimeters and record the data below and in the review section at the end of the exercise.

? Near point of right eye: _____   1

? Near point of left eye: _____   2

Measurement of the Distribution of Rods and Cones

To determine the distribution of rods and cones, have your lab partner look straight ahead. Slowly move a small colored object (a pen, piece of chalk, comb, etc.), without letting your lab partner see it, from the back of your lab partner's head, around the side, toward the front. With your lab partner still looking straight ahead, note the approximate angle when your lab partner is able to see the object (the use of rods). Your lab partner should keep his or her eyes directed forward. Continue to move the object forward slowly until recognition of the color of the object occurs. Note the approximate angle from the tip of the nose. You can record the approximate angle by using an apparatus called a Vision Disk or by placing a protractor above your lab partner's head while you make your measurements. Record these below and in the review section.

❓ Angle where object is perceived: _____ 3

❓ Angle where color is determined: _____ 4

What is the difference in the distribution of rods and cones in the eye?

❓ Rod distribution: _____ 5

❓ Cone distribution: _____ 6

When you are intently focusing on a subject, what cell type (rods or cones) are you using?

Measurement of Binocular Visual Field

Not all animals have the same **visual field.** Some prey species (such as deer or sheep) have extensive visual fields, with little binocular vision. On the other hand, many predators, birds, and arboreal animals have a more limited visual field, yet they have greater **binocular,** or **stereoscopic, vision.** Binocular vision allows arboreal animals to perceive depth—vital when judging how far away the next branch is! You can determine your visual

field with the use of a Vision Disk or protractor. If you are using a Vision Disk, follow the instructions enclosed. If not, sit down and have your lab partner stand behind you. Close your right eye and look straight ahead with the left. While the right eye is closed, have your lab partner move an object (pen, paper disk, etc.) from behind your head from the left until you can just see the object. Measure the angle from the tip of the nose to where you see the object. This is illustrated in figure 26.9 ("Angle A"). With the same eye directed ahead, continue moving the object until it is out of view (to the right of the nose somewhere). This is illustrated in figure 26.9 ("Angle B"). Determine the angle from the nose to where the object disappears. Add these two values and record the result below and in the review section.

❓ Angle where object is perceived: _____ 7

❓ Angle where object disappears: _____ 8

Now close your left eye and repeat the exercise on the right side. This is illustrated in figure 26.9 ("Angle C" and "Angle D"). Determine the total visual field for each eye by adding the sum of figure 26.9, "Angle A" and "Angle B," for the left eye and the sum of "Angle C" and "Angle D" for the right eye. For both eyes, add the sum of "Angle A" and "Angle C," and for the degree of overlap between the eyes, "Angle B" and "Angle D" (see figure 26.10). Record these data in the following spaces and in the review section.

❓ Visual field of right eye: _____ 9

❓ Visual field of left eye: _____ 10

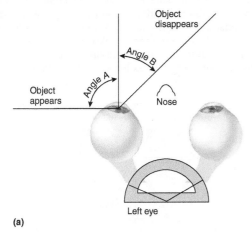
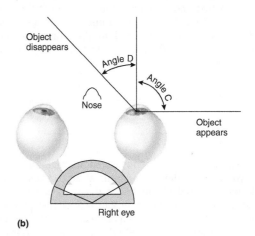

(a)   **(b)**

FIGURE 26.9 **Measuring the Visual Field** (a) Left eye; (b) right eye.

346　**LABORATORY 26**　Eye and Vision

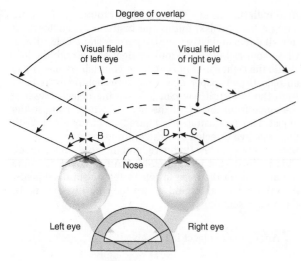

FIGURE 26.10 **Visual Field**

❓ Complete visual field of both eyes: _____ 11

❓ Degree of overlap: _____ 12

Measurement of Visual Acuity (Snellen Test)

Face the Snellen eye chart from 20 feet away and have your lab partner stand next to the chart. Cover one eye with a 3-by-5-inch card and have your lab partner point to the largest letter on the chart. Do *not* read the chart with both eyes open. Your lab partner should then progressively move down the chart and *note the line that has the smallest print in which you made no errors.* Your lab partner should record the numbers at the side of the line (such as 20/20). These numbers refer to your **visual acuity.** Switch the card to the other eye and repeat the test. Record your results below and in the review section.

❓ Left eye: _____ 13

❓ Right eye: _____ 14

A vision of 20/20 is considered normal. In 20/20 vision you can see the same details at 20 feet that other people with normal vision see at the same distance. If your vision is 20/15, then you can see at 20 feet what people with normal vision see at 15 feet. If your vision is 20/100, then you see at 20 feet what people with normal vision see at 100 feet.

Astigmatism Tests

If the cornea or lens of the human eye were perfectly smooth, the incoming image would strike the retina evenly and there would be no blurry areas. In most people the cornea or lens is not perfectly smooth, and this is known as astigmatism. In a normal optical exam the distance correction is made first (to determine visual acuity) and then, with the corrective lenses in place, an astigmatism test is performed.

If you do not normally wear corrective lenses, then cover one eye and examine the astigmatism chart (as represented in figure 26.11) from 20 feet away. The chart consists of a series of parallel lines radiating from the center. Stare at the center of the chart and determine which of the sets of parallel lines, if any, appears light or blurry. Have your lab partner note the corresponding number on the chart and record the number below and in the review section.

❓ Astigmatism numbers: _____ 15

If you wear corrective lenses, then not only is the condition of nearsightedness or farsightedness corrected but astigmatism is corrected also. To test for astigmatism move about 12 feet from the chart, hold your glasses slightly away from your face, and then rotate them 90 degrees. If your glasses normally correct for astigmatism, the lines on the chart will be blurry as you rotate your glasses.

Ophthalmoscope

Clinical use of the ophthalmoscope is important not only for the diagnosis of variances in the eyeball but also as a potential indicator of diseases, such as **diabetes mellitus,** that may affect the eye. Familiarize yourself with the parts of the ophthalmoscope (see figure 26.12). Locate the ring (rheostat control) at the top of the handle. Depress the button and turn the ring until the light comes on. The head piece of the ophthalmoscope consists of a rotating disc of lenses. You can change the diopter (strength) of the lenses by rotating the disc clockwise or counterclockwise. As the numbers get progressively larger, you are looking through more convex lenses. If you rotate the disc

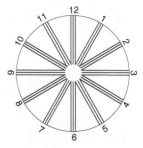

FIGURE 26.11 **Astigmatism Chart**

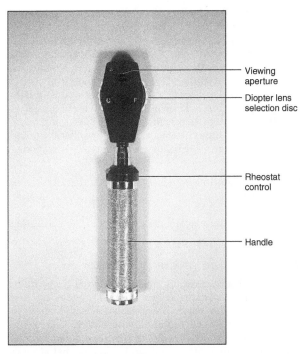

FIGURE 26.12 **Ophthalmoscope**

Viewing aperture

Diopter lens selection disc

Rheostat control

Handle

FIGURE 26.13 **Use of Ophthalmoscope**

in the other direction, the lenses become more concave. At the zero reading there are no lenses in place.

Observation with the Ophthalmoscope

Caution!   Examine the posterior region of the eye only for a short time. Extensive use of the ophthalmoscope can damage the eye.

Sit facing your lab partner. Select the left eye to examine. Have the ophthalmoscope setting at zero and use your left hand to hold the ophthalmoscope. Use your left eye to look through the ophthalmoscope and move in close to examine the eye of your lab partner (see figure 26.13). You may rest your hand on the cheek of your lab partner if you need to steady your hand. Look into the pupil and examine the back of the eye. If the back appears fuzzy, rotate the disc clockwise (positive diopters) and see if it comes into focus. If a positive setting provides a clear view of the eye, then your lab partner has **hyperopia** (hypermetropic vision), or farsightedness. In farsightedness the eyeball is too short and the image is focused posterior to the retina. Positive diopter lenses focus the image on the retina. If the image is indistinct, then adjust the disc counterclockwise to obtain a negative diopter reading. If the image is clear with a negative number, then your lab partner has **myopia** (myopic vision), or nearsightedness. In nearsightedness the

eyeball is too long and lenses with negative diopters focus the images farther back on the retina. This procedure is based on the assumption that your vision, as the examiner, is normal. Examine the retina of the eye and notice the blood vessels there.

Pupillary Reactions

Have your lab partner sit in a dark room for a minute or two. Examine his or her eyes in dim light. Are the pupils dilated or constricted? Record the data below and in the review section.

❓ Pupil diameter in dim light: _____ 16

Shine a penlight in the right eye. Record what happens to the pupil diameter.

❓ Right pupil diameter: _____ 17

As you shine the light into the right eye, what occurs in the left pupil? This is called a **consensual reflex.** Record the effect.

❓ Left pupil diameter: _____ 18

Color Blindness

Color vision is dependent on three separate cone cell sensitivities. Cones may be red, green, or blue sensitive. Changes in the genes on the X chromosome are the most common cause of color blindness. Some individuals may be unable to see a particular color, while others may have a reduction in their ability to see a particular color. Color blindness is most common in males and relatively rare in females. This is due to the chromosomal makeup of the two sexes. The male chromosome makeup is XY. The Y chromosome does not carry the gene for color vision. If the X chromosome carries a gene for color blindness, then the male exhibits color blindness. On the other hand, if a female carries the gene for color blindness on the X chromosome, the chances are that she will have a normal gene on the other X chromosome. The normal gene is expressed, cone pigments are produced, and the female has normal color vision.

You can test for color blindness by matching various samples of colored yarn with a presented test sample or you can use Ishihara color charts, as represented in figure 26.14. If you use the color charts, flip through the book with a lab partner and record which charts were accurately viewed and which plates, if any, were missed. You can calculate the type of color blindness and the degree by following your instructor's directions or those that come with the color chart. Record your data below and in the review section.

❓ Your color vision: _____ 19

Afterimages

The photosensitive pigment of the rods is called **rhodopsin,** which is composed of light-sensitive **retinal** (a vitamin A derivative) and the protein **opsin.** When light strikes the retina, the purple-colored rhodopsin splits into its two component parts and becomes pale (a process known as "bleaching"). You can test the time for separation and reassembly of the photopigments by staring at a contrasting image on a card under a moderately bright lightbulb (60 watt) for a few moments. Stare long enough to get an image (about 10 to 20 seconds) and then shut your eyes. Have your lab partner record the time. You should see a colored image against a dark background. This is known as a positive afterimage, due to the photoreceptors continuously firing. After a few moments you should see the reverse of the original image (dark against a light background). This is known as a negative afterimage. A negative afterimage reflects the bleaching effects of rhodopsin. Record the time change for the positive afterimage and the negative afterimage below and in the review section.

❓ Positive afterimage: _____ 20

❓ Negative afterimage: _____ 21

Determination of the Blind Spot

The **optic disc** is a region where the retinal nerve fibers exit from the back of the eye and form the **optic nerve.** The mass exit of the nerve fibers leaves a small circle at the back of the eye devoid of photoreceptors. This region, the optic disc, is also known as the **blind spot.** You can locate the blind spot by holding this lab manual at arm's length. Use your right eye (close your left eye) and stare at the following χ. It should be in line with the middle of your nose. *Slowly* move the manual closer to you and stare only at the χ. At a particular distance the dot disappears.

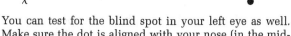

You can test for the blind spot in your left eye as well. Make sure the dot is aligned with your nose (in the midsagittal plane).

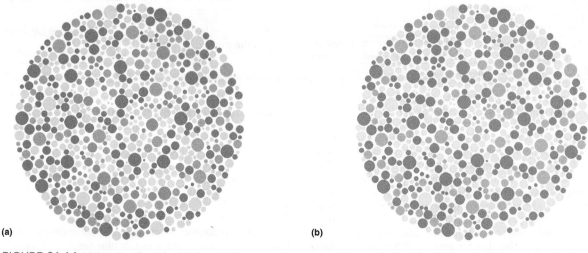

(a)   (b)

FIGURE 26.14 Ishihara Test for Color Blindness (a) Plate as seen by a person with normal color vision; (b) plate as seen by a person who has red-green color blindness.

EXERCISE

26

REVIEW SECTION ■connect
|ANATOMY & PHYSIOLOGY

Eye and Vision

Name _____ *Date* _____

Lab Section _____ *Time* _____

Review Questions

1. Eye shine in nocturnal mammals is different from the "red eye" seen in some flash photographs. Eye shine is the reflection from the tapetum lucidum. What might produce "red eye"?

2. Fill in the following illustration using the terms provided.

lens	retina	anterior cavity (anterior chamber)
sclera	optic nerve	choroid
ciliary body	cornea	pupil
		suspensory ligaments

a. _____

b. _____

c. _____

d. _____

e. _____

f. _____

g. _____

h. _____ (the space)

i. _____

f. _____ (the space)

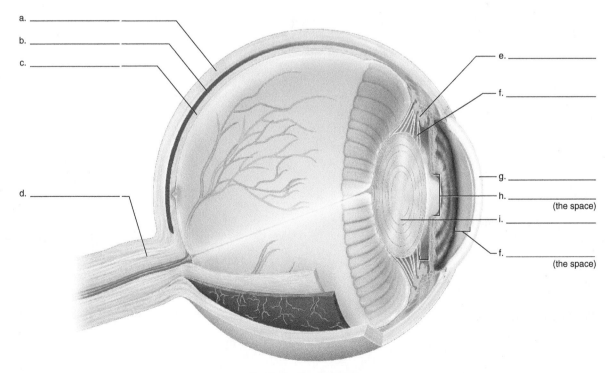

Sagittal section of the eye

350   **REVIEW 26**   Eye and Vision

3. Since the lens is made of protein, what effect might the preserving fluid used in lab have on the structure of the lens? How would this affect the clarity?

4. What is the consensual reflex of the pupil?

5. How does the vitreous body differ from the aqueous humor in location and viscosity?

6. What layer of the eye converts visible light into nerve impulses?

7. What nerve is composed of axons of the ganglion cells and transmits action potentials to the thalamus of the brain?

8. What is another name for the sclera?

9. How would you define an extrinsic muscle of the eye?

10. What gland produces tears?

11. What is the name of the transparent layer of the eye in front of the anterior chamber?

12. The iris of the eye has two main types of muscles. Name these two muscles and how they affect the pupil.

13. Where is the vitreous body found?

14. What is the function of the choroid?

15. Is the lens anterior or posterior to the iris?

16. Which retinal cells are responsible for vision in dim light?

17. How would you define the near point of the eye?

18. What do the numbers 20/100 mean for visual acuity?

352   **REVIEW 26**   Eye and Vision

19. What is an astigmatism?

20. In what area of the eye is the blind spot located? Why is it called the blind spot?

21. Label the following illustration.

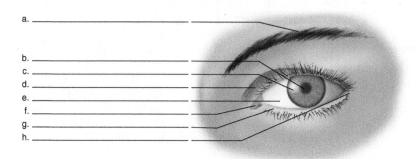

a. _____

b. _____
c. _____
d. _____
e. _____
f. _____
g. _____
h. _____

?Chapter Summary Data

Use this section to record your results from questions within the exercise.

1. _____   12. _____
2. _____   13. _____
3. _____   14. _____
4. _____   15. _____
5. _____   16. _____
6. _____   17. _____
7. _____   18. _____
8. _____   19. _____
9. _____   20. _____
10. _____   21. _____
11. _____

LABORATORY

Ear, Hearing, and Equilibrium

INTRODUCTION

The ear is a complex sense organ that performs two major functions, hearing and equilibrium. It consists of three regions, an outer ear, a middle ear, and an inner ear. The structure and function of the ear are covered in the Saladin text in chapter 16, "Sense Organs." Hearing is considered **mechanoreception,** because the ear receives mechanical vibrations (sound waves) and translates them into nerve impulses. This process begins with the vibrations reaching the outer ear and ends up being interpreted as sound in the temporal lobe of the brain. Equilibrium, on the other hand, involves receptors in the inner ear, along with other sensory perceptions, such as visual cues from the eye, and **proprioreception** in joints. There are two types of equilibrium sensed by the inner ear. These are **static equilibrium** and **dynamic equilibrium.** In static equilibrium an individual is able to determine his or her nonmoving position (such as standing upright or lying down). In dynamic equilibrium motion is detected. Sudden acceleration, abrupt turning, and spinning are examples of dynamic equilibrium.

OBJECTIVES

At the end of this exercise you should be able to

1. explain how mechanical sound vibrations are translated into nerve impulses;
2. list the structures of the outer, middle, and inner ear;
3. describe the structure of the cochlea;
4. perform conduction deafness tests, such as the Rinne and Weber tests;
5. compare dynamic and static equilibrium and the structures involved in their perception.
6. describe the value of postural reflexes with regard to living in a dynamic environment.

MATERIALS

Models and charts of the ear

Microscope

Slides of the cochlea

Tuning fork (256 Hz)

Rubber reflex hammer

Audiometer

Cotton balls

Model of ear ossicles

Meter stick

Ticking stopwatch

Bright desk lamp

Swivel chair

PROCEDURE

Anatomy of the Ear

The ear can be divided into three regions, the **outer (external), middle,** and **inner ear.** The outer ear consists of those auditory structures superficial to the **tympanic membrane (eardrum).** The middle ear contains the ear **ossicles (bones)** and **auditory (Eustachian) tube,** and the inner ear consists of the **cochlea, vestibule,** and **semicircular ducts.** Examine the charts and models in lab and compare them with figure 27.1 as you read about the individual regions of the ear.

Structure of the Outer Ear

The outer ear consists of the **pinna (auricle),** which can further be subdivided into the **helix** and the **earlobe (lobule).** The helix is composed of stratified squamous

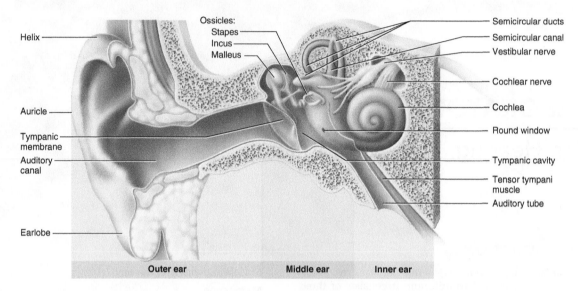

FIGURE 27.1 **Anatomy of the Ear**

epithelium overlying elastic cartilage. This cartilage allows the ears to bend significantly. Deep to the pinna the external ear forms the **auditory canal,** which penetrates into the temporal bone.

Structure of the Middle Ear

The tympanic membrane is the border between the outer ear and the middle ear. It is composed of connective tissue covered by epithelial tissue. The membrane is sensitive to sound and vibrates as sound is funneled down the auditory canal. The middle ear consists of a main cavity known as the **tympanic cavity;** three small bones, or **ossicles;** and the auditory tube (see figure 27.1). The ossicle attached to the tympanic membrane is the **malleus** (*malleus* = hammer). The malleus is attached to the **incus** (*incus* = anvil), which is attached to the **stapes** (*stapes* = stirrup).

Sound consists of pressure waves. As these waves strike the tympanic membrane, it vibrates. This vibration is conducted by the ossicles to the oval window. The process of moving from a large-diameter structure (tympanic membrane) to a smaller-diameter structure (oval window) magnifies the sound about 18 times. See figure 27.2. Examine the ossicles in figure 27.1 and on models in the lab. In addition to the ossicles the **auditory tube** (Eustachian tube) occurs in the middle ear. This tube connects the middle ear to the nasopharynx (see figure 27.1) and equalizes pressure between the middle ear and the external environment when changes of pressure occur (such as during changes of elevation). The auditory tube can be a conduit for microorganisms that travel from the nasopharynx to the middle ear and lead to middle-ear infections, particularly in young children.

Structure of the Inner Ear

The inner ear is encased in two labyrinthine structures and filled with two separate fluids. The outermost structure is the **bony labyrinth.** Inside the bony labyrinth is **perilymph,** a clear fluid external to the **membranous labyrinth.** The fluid enclosed by the membranous labyrinth is the **endolymph,** important in both hearing and equilibrium. The membranous labyrinth is enclosed inside the bony labyrinth like a tube within a tube.

The inner ear is a complex structure composed of three regions, the cochlea, the vestibule, and the semicircular ducts (see figures 27.1 and 27.3). The cochlea is a spiral

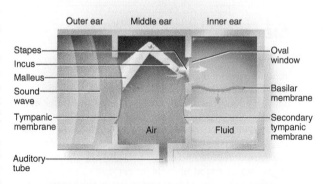

FIGURE 27.2 **Model of Hearing** Pressure waves of sound vibrate the tympanic membrane, which transfers sound to the oval window and finally to the basilar membrane, where vibration is converted to neural impulses.

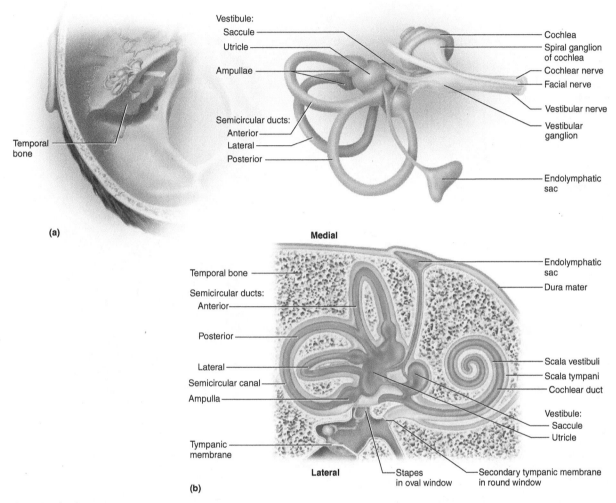

Medial

Vestibule:
Saccule
Utricle
Ampullae

Semicircular ducts:
Anterior
Lateral
Posterior

Temporal
bone

Cochlea
Spiral ganglion
of cochlea
Cochlear nerve
Facial nerve
Vestibular nerve
Vestibular
ganglion

Endolymphatic
sac

(a)

Temporal bone

Semicircular ducts:
Anterior

Posterior

Lateral
Semicircular canal
Ampulla

Tympanic
membrane

Endolymphatic
sac
Dura mater

Scala vestibuli
Scala tympani
Cochlear duct

Vestibule:
Saccule
Utricle

Lateral   Stapes   Secondary tympanic membrane
                   in oval window   in round window

(b)

FIGURE 27.3 **Anatomy of the Inner Ear** (a) Major regions of the inner ear; (b) relationship of membranous labyrinth to bony labyrinth.

structure that resembles a seashell (*cochlea* = snail), while the semicircular ducts look like three loops. Between these two structures is the vestibule.

Cochlea The cochlea (see figures 27.1, 27.3, and 27.4) is involved in hearing. As the sound waves travel down the auditory canal they cause the tympanic membrane to vibrate. This vibration rocks the ear ossicles, which are connected to the inner ear. As the stapes vibrates it moves back and forth in the **oval window,** and this causes fluid to move back and forth in the cochlea. The cochlea also has a **round window** with a secondary tympanic membrane, which allows the pressure wave from the ossicles to move fluid. Sound waves are measured by their amplitude (loudness) and wavelength (pitch). The wavelengths are measured in cycles per second, also known as hertz (Hz). The human

ear is capable of hearing high-pitched sounds up to 20,000 Hz and sounds as low as about 20 Hz. High-pitched sounds with vibrations of short wavelength, up to 20,000 Hz in the human ear, stimulate the region of the cochlea closest to the middle ear. Low-pitched sounds with longer wavelengths, down to 20 Hz, stimulate the region of the cochlea farther from the middle ear. In this way the cochlea can perceive sounds of varying wavelengths at the same time.

Examine a microscopic section of the cochlea in cross section. There are chambers clustered in threes. Find the **scala vestibuli, cochlear duct (scala media),** and **scala tympani** on the microscope slide. Compare these to figures 27.4 and 27.5.

Note the **spiral organ (acoustic organ,** or **organ of Corti)** in the area between the **vestibular membrane** and the **basilar membrane.** The spiral organ in figure 27.5

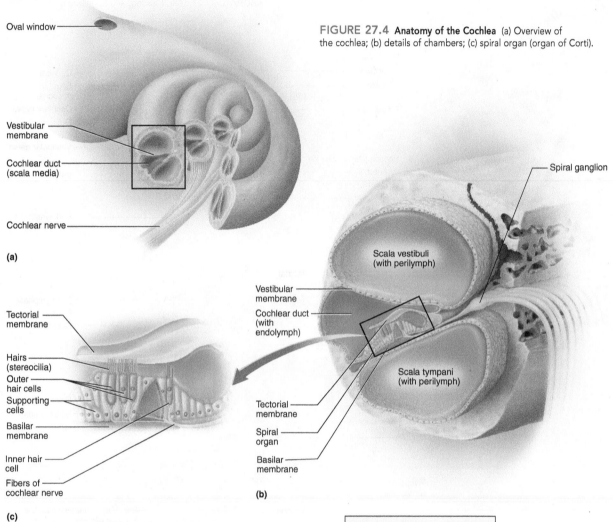

FIGURE 27.4 **Anatomy of the Cochlea** (a) Overview of the cochlea; (b) details of chambers; (c) spiral organ (organ of Corti).

is seen in cross section, but remember that it runs the length of the cochlea. The spiral organ is sensitive to sound waves. As a particular region of the spiral organ is stimulated, the basilar membrane vibrates. This bends the cilia that connect the hair cells to the tectorial membrane. The hair cells send impulses to the cochlear branch of the **vestibulocochlear nerve.** These impulses travel to the **auditory cortex** of the **temporal lobe,** where they are interpreted as sound (see figure 27.6).

Vestibule   Another part of the inner ear is the vestibule. The **vestibule** consists of the **utricle** and **saccule** (see figures 27.3 and 27.7). These two chambers are involved in the interpretation of static equilibrium and linear acceleration. The utricle and saccule have regions known as maculae, which consist of hair cells with stereocilia and a kinocilium grouped together in a gelatinous mass called the otolithic membrane and weighted with calcium carbonate stones called **otoliths.** These can be seen in

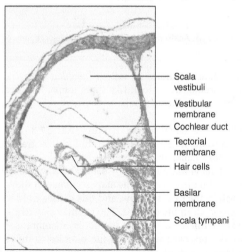

FIGURE 27.5 **Photomicrograph of Cross Section of the Cochlea** (100×)

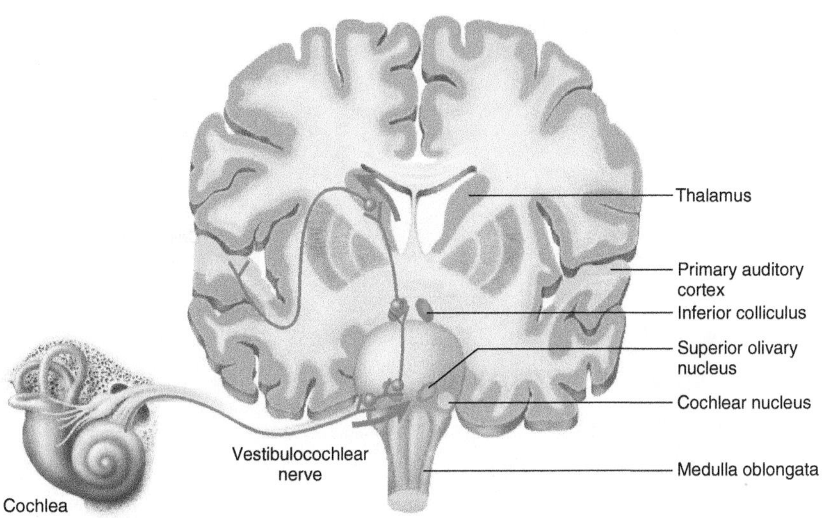

FIGURE 27.6 **Interpretive Pathway of Hearing** Sound impulses from the cochlea travel via nerves and tracts to the primary auditory cortex.

Thalamus

Primary auditory cortex

Inferior colliculus

Superior olivary nucleus

Cochlear nucleus

Medulla oblongata

Vestibulocochlear nerve

Cochlea

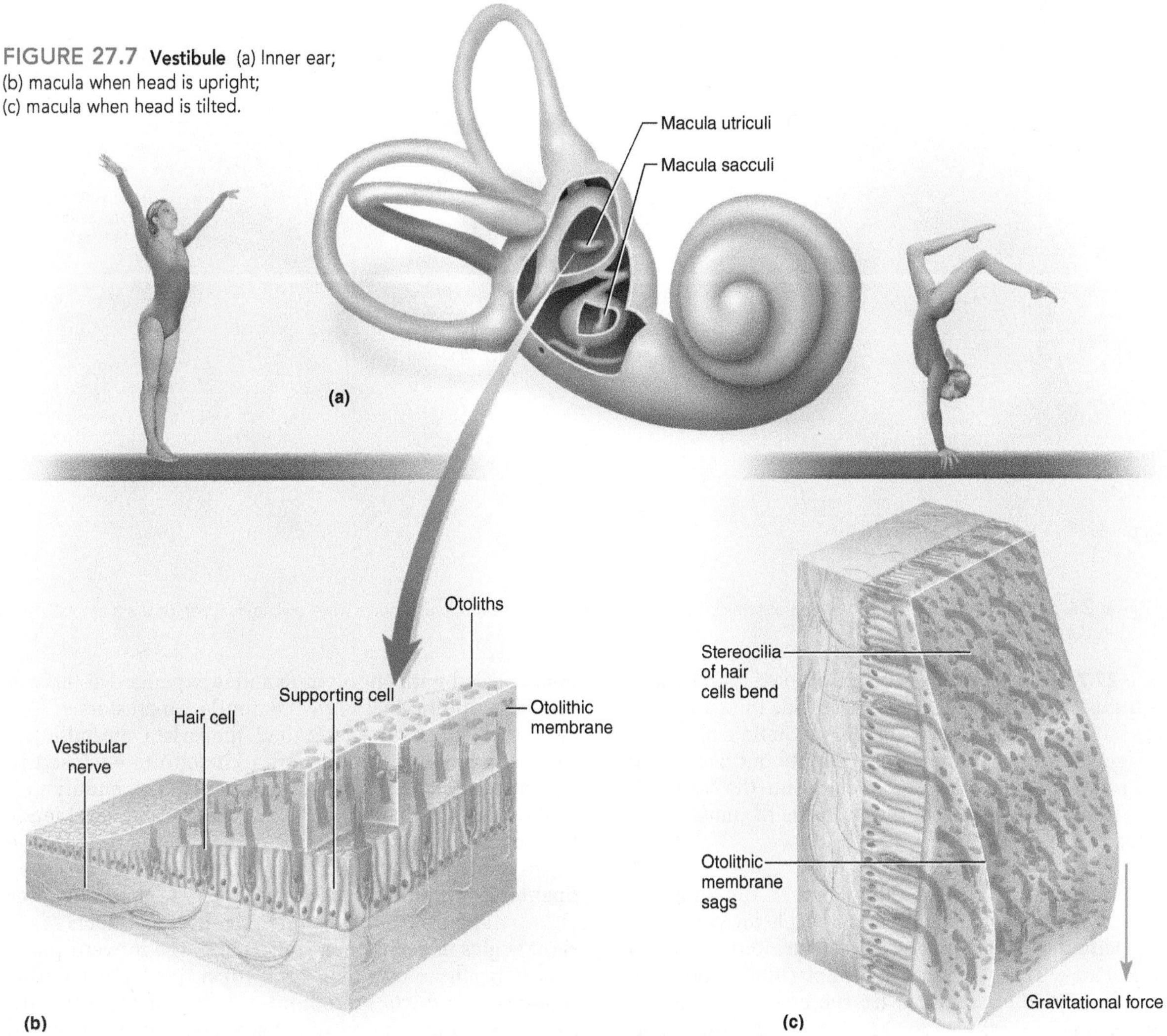

FIGURE 27.7 **Vestibule** (a) Inner ear; (b) macula when head is upright; (c) macula when head is tilted.

Macula utriculi

Macula sacculi

(a)

Otoliths

Supporting cell

Otolithic membrane

Hair cell

Vestibular nerve

Stereocilia of hair cells bend

Otolithic membrane sags

Gravitational force

(b)

(c)

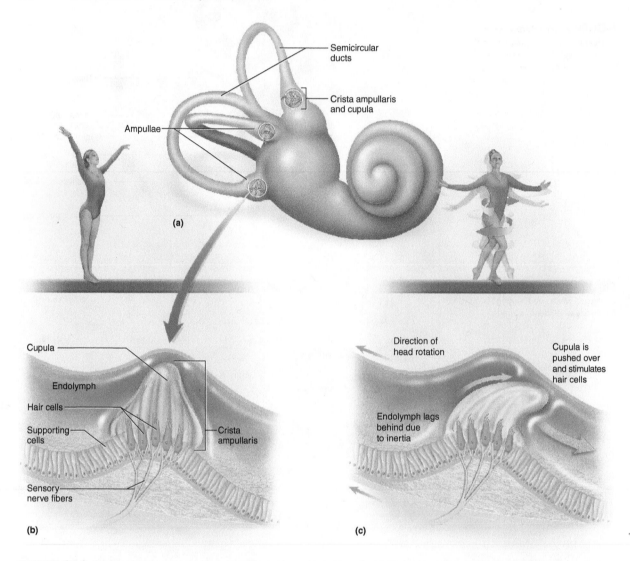

FIGURE 27.8 Semicircular Ducts (a) Position of semicircular ducts; (b) position of semicircular ducts when still; (c) function of crista ampullaris and cupula during movement.

figure 27.7. As the head is accelerated or tipped by gravity, the otoliths cause the cilia to bend, indicating that the position of the head has changed. Static equilibrium is perceived not only from the vestibule but from visual cues as well. When the visual cues and the vestibular cues are not synchronized, then a sense of imbalance or nausea can occur.

Semicircular Ducts The third part of the inner ear consists of the **semicircular ducts,** each located inside a semicircular canal, involved in determining dynamic equilibrium. There are three semicircular ducts, each at 90 degrees to one another (in the horizontal, sagittal, and coronal planes) (see figure 27.8). Each semicircular

duct is filled with endolymph and is expanded at its base into an **ampulla.** Inside each ampulla are clusters of hair cells and support cells (called the **crista ampullaris).** The cells have stereocilia and a kinocilium enclosed in a gelatinous material called the **cupula.** The endolymph in the membranous labyrinth has inertia; that is, it tends to remain in the same place. As the head is rotated, the endolymph pushes against the **stereocilia.** In this way **angular** or **rotational** acceleration can be determined as shown in figure 27.8c. The three semicircular ducts are at right angles to each other. If motion in the forward plane occurs (such as by doing back flips), then the **anterior semicircular ducts** are stimulated. If you were to turn cartwheels, then the **posterior semicircular ducts** would be stimulated. If you were to spin around on your heels, then the **lateral semicircular ducts** would pick up the information.

Hearing Tests

Obtain a meter stick and a ticking stopwatch. Have your lab partner sit in a quiet room and slowly move the ticking watch away from one of his or her ears until the sound can no longer be heard. Record the distance in centimeters (when the sound can no longer be heard) in the space provided and in the review section. Check the other ear and record the data.

? Maximum distance sound perceived for right ear:

_____ 1

? Maximum distance sound perceived for left ear:

_____ 2

Audiometer Test

Sound frequency (pitch) is measured in hertz and sound energy (loudness) is measured in units called **decibels** (dB). The threshold of hearing is the quietest sound a person with normal hearing can perceive at any particular frequency. The standard measurement of the threshold of hearing is zero decibels at 1,000 Hz. This does not mean that there is no sound energy below zero decibels but rather that humans cannot perceive sound below that value. Decibels are measured on a logarithmic scale, so for each 10 dB increase in sound 10 times more energy is produced. Therefore 30 dB is 10 times louder than 20 dB but 40 dB is 100 times louder than 20 dB.

In clinical settings, a tuning fork test is frequently performed to asses a person's hearing and, if it appears that there is hearing loss, a more refined test using an audiometer may be suggested. Audiometry involves the use of a machine (an audiometer) that can produce sounds of single frequency at different decibels.

Ask your instructor to demonstrate how to use an audiometer to test hearing. Age-related hearing loss (presbycusis) (pres-bee-CUE-sis) is a progressive condition that affects many older adults, though hearing loss is greatly accelerated by loud music, moderate to extensive headphone use, and exposure to machines that operate at high decibel levels. Another common source of hearing loss is the use of recreational firearms without hearing protection.

Measuring Hearing

Normal hearing ranges typically from 0–20 dB in frequencies ranging from 500–4,000 Hz. Mild hearing loss is from 20–40 dB, moderate hearing loss is from 40–60 dB, and severe hearing loss is greater than 60 dB. To measure this value set the audiometer to 500 Hz and then lower the level in 10 dB increments from 50 dB to the point where your lab partner can no longer hear the tone. Record the threshold for hearing. Test other frequencies as well, as listed below. Hearing loss is significant when the hearing threshold is at 20 dB or more at any two frequencies in an ear or 30 dB at any particular frequency. Record the minimum sound levels.

Right Ear	Left Ear
500: _____	_____
1,000: _____	_____
2,000: _____	_____
4,000: _____	_____

The audiometer test is not specifically a gauge to determine whether the hearing loss is due to **conduction hearing loss,** where the tympanic membrane or ear ossicles may be damaged, or **sensorineural hearing loss,** where the damage may occur in the cochlea, vestibulocochlear nerve, or temporal lobe of the brain. Several tests have been used to determine which type of hearing loss may be involved.

Weber Test

Conduction deafness occurs when damage to the tympanic membrane or ear ossicles is present. You can test for this type of deafness with a tuning fork. Hold on to the handle of a 256 Hz (middle C) tuning fork. Strike the tines (the forked portion) on a solid surface and gently place the end of the handle on your lab partner's chin or forehead (see figure 27.9).

If the sound is louder in one ear, then this may be a sign of conduction deafness. In this case the affected ear

FIGURE 27.9 **Weber Test**

is not picking up sounds from the tympanic membrane and is more sensitive to vibrations coming through the skull bones. The sound will be louder in the ear that has conduction deafness. If the ear has nerve damage, then the sound will be louder in the normal ear. Record your results in the following space and in the review section.

? Sound perception (right/left or equal in both ears):

____________________________________ 3

To simulate conductive hearing loss with the Weber test, have your lab partner close off one ear with the pad of a finger, strike the tuning fork, and place it on your lab partner's forehead. When the ear canal is closed the sound will be louder in that ear.

Rinne Test

Strike the tuning fork and place the handle on the mastoid process. When your lab partner indicates that the sound disappears, lift the tuning fork from the mastoid process and bring it to the outside of the pinna (see figure 27.10). Can the sound now be heard? If the sound cannot be heard after the tuning fork is placed near the outside of the ear, then there is damage to the tympanic membrane or ear ossicles (conduction deafness), a positive Rinne test. This may also be due to obstructions in the ear canal (such as earwax). The sound is normally louder in air because of the amplification from the tympanic membrane to the oval window. Record your results in the following spaces and in the review section.

? Right ear: ____________________________ 4

? Left ear: ____________________________ 5

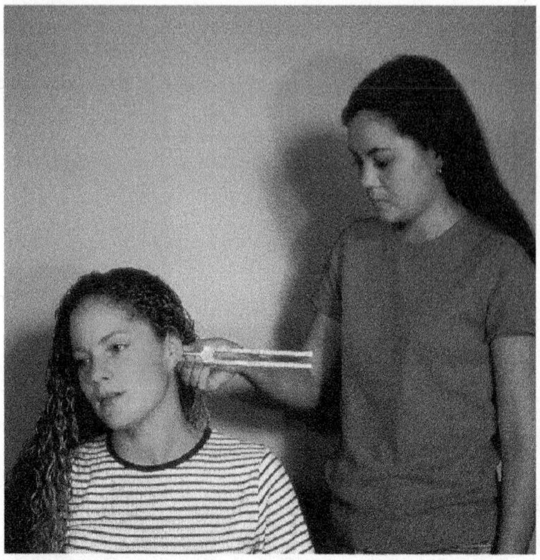

FIGURE 27.10 **Rinne Test**

Bing Test

Another hearing test that examines hearing loss is the Bing test. Strike the tuning fork and place it on the mastoid process as you did with the Rinne test. With your other hand close off the auditory canal with the pad of a finger. A person with normal hearing or one with sensoneurial hearing loss will hear the sound better when the ear canal is closed. This is a **positive Bing test.** A person with conductive hearing loss will not notice a change in sound. This is a **negative Bing test.** Record your results in the following space and in the section at the end of the exercise.

? Results from the Bing test: ________________________ 6

Sound Location

Have your lab partner sit with eyes closed. Strike the tuning fork with a rubber reflex hammer above his or her head. Have your lab partner describe to you where the sound is located. Strike the tuning fork behind the head, to each side, in front, and below the chin of your lab partner. Record the results in the following chart.

Location Where Sound Was Struck	Where Sound Was Perceived
Above head	
Behind head	
Right side	
Left side	
In front of head	
Below chin	

Postural Reflex Test

Unexpected changes that move the body away from a state of equilibrium cause postural reflexes that compensate for that change. If you are facing forward on a boat and it begins to tilt to the starboard (right), your body compensates and moves to the left.

Postural reflexes are important for maintaining the upright position of the body. These reflexes are negative-feedback mechanisms. If, for example, you lean slightly to the left, your left foot abducts to regain the center of balance.

1. Select an area free from any obstacles.
2. While you read this manual, stand on your tiptoes. Your lab partner should give you a little nudge to the left or right (not enough to knock you off your feet) to push you off balance. The postural reflex is reflected in the movement of the foot on the opposite side of your lab partner. If you are nudged to the left, then your left foot should move to the side to

correct against the direction of the contact. Did your postural reflex work?

3. Record your result in the following space and in the review section.

❓ Postural reflex: _____ 7

Barany's Test

Barany's test examines visual responses to changes in dynamic equilibrium. As the head turns, one of the reflexes that occurs is movement of the eyes in the opposite direction of the rotation. Nerve impulses from the semicircular canals innervate the eye muscles and cause the eye movement. When rotating in one direction, the eyes move in the opposite direction, so that there is enough time for a visual image to be fixed. The volunteer for this test should not be subject to dizziness or nausea.

1. Place the subject in a swivel chair with four or five students close by, standing in a circle, in case the subject loses balance and begins to fall. The student chosen for this exercise should grab onto the chair firmly so as not to fall off. The subject should tilt his or her head forward about 30 degrees, which will place the lateral semicircular ducts horizontally for maximum stimulation.
2. One member of the group should spin the chair around about 10 revolutions while the subject keeps his or her eyes open.
3. Stop the chair and have the subject look forward. The twitching of the eyes is called **nystagmus** and is due to the stimulation of the endolymph flowing in the semicircular ducts. When the chair is stopped the fluid in the endolymph will have overcome the inertia and will continue to flow in the ducts.

Did the movement of the eyes occur in the direction of the rotation or in the opposite direction? Record your results in the following space and in the review section.

❓ Direction of chair rotation relative to subject: _____ 8

❓ Direction of eye rotation: _____ 9

Romberg Test

The Romberg test involves testing the static equilibrium function of the body. This should be done in pairs. An observer watches the degree of sway of the subject who stands near a wall or blackboard.

1. Place the subject with his or her back to the blackboard or any surface on which you can see the shadow of the subject. Use a desk lamp, if needed.
2. Have the subject stand in that direction for 1 minute and determine if there are any exaggerated movements to the left or right. The subject should not rest against the wall.
3. Record your results in the following space and in the review section.

❓ Amount of lateral sway: _____ 10

You should then have your lab partner close his or her eyes (to reduce visual cues) and repeat the test. Is the swaying motion increased or decreased? Record your results in the following space.

❓ Amount of lateral sway with eyes closed: _____ 11

Notes

REVIEW SECTION ▓connect
|ANATOMY & PHYSIOLOGY

Ear, Hearing, and Equilibrium

Name _____   Date _____

Lab Section _____   Time _____

Review Questions

1. What are the three general areas or regions of the ear?

2. The pinna of the ear consists of what two main parts?

3. To what sense modality (or modalities) does the ear respond?

4. The ear performs two major sensory functions. What are they?

5. What structure separates the outer ear from the middle ear?

6. Trace the pathway of sound waves (pressure waves) from the outer ear to the inner ear.

364   **REVIEW 27** Ear, Hearing, and Equilibrium

7. From the following choices, select the function of the cochlea.
   a. static equilibrium
   b. taste
   c. hearing
   d. dynamic equilibrium

8. What area is found between the scala vestibuli and the scala tympani?

9. What is the name of the nerve that carries signals from the cochlea and vestibule to the brain?

10. What units are used to measure sound energy?

11. What part of the inner ear is involved in transmitting signals of static equilibrium?

12. Name the parts of the ear that might be impaired if a person demonstrates conduction deafness.

13. What two diagnostic tests are used to determine conduction deafness?

14. What is the name of the canal that runs from the auricle to the tympanic membrane?

15. How would you differentiate conductive hearing loss from sensorineural hearing loss based on hearing tests?

16. What tube between the middle ear and the nasopharynx is responsible for the equalization of pressure when you change elevation?

17. What is the name of the space that encloses the ear ossicles?

18. Name the ear ossicles in sequence from the tympanic membrane to the oval window.

19. Name all the parts of the inner ear.

20. Background noise affects hearing tests. In the ticking watch test, what type of result, in terms of auditory sensitivity, would you have recorded if moderate background noise were present?

21. In the Weber test, the ear that perceives the sound as being louder is the deaf ear. Why is this the case?

366   **REVIEW 27**   Ear, Hearing, and Equilibrium

22. Fill in the following illustration of the ear using the terms provided.

cochlea
ear ossicles
auditory canal
auditory tube
tympanic membrane
semicircular ducts

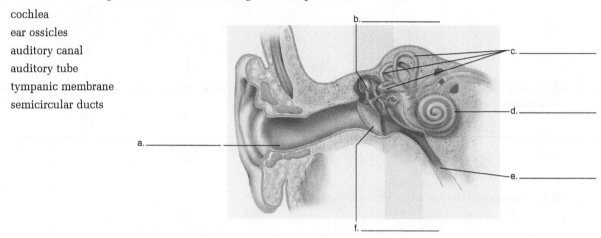

23. Label the following illustration of the cross section of cochlea using the terms provided.

hair cells
scala tympani
tectorial membrane
scala vestibuli
vestibular membrane
scala media (cochlear duct)

? Chapter Summary Data

Use this section to record your results from questions within the exercise.

1. _____   7. _____

2. _____   8. _____

3. _____   9. _____

4. _____   10. _____

5. _____   11. _____

6. _____

29

LABORATORY

Blood

INTRODUCTION

Blood is a connective tissue that consists of two parts, formed elements and plasma. Formed elements make up about 45% of the blood volume and are further subdivided into erythrocytes (red blood cells), leukocytes (white blood cells), and platelets (thrombocytes). Platelets are not cells, and this is why the fraction of blood is called formed elements and not blood cells.

Plasma constitutes approximately 55% of the blood volume and contains water, lipids, dissolved substances, colloidal proteins, and clotting factors.

The study of blood cells is important because it is the fluid medium of the cardiovascular system and because it has significant clinical implications. Changes in the numbers and types of blood cells may be used as indicators of disease. In this exercise you examine the nature of blood cells, discussed in the Saladin text in chapter 18, "The Circulatory System: Blood."

Caution! The risk of blood-borne diseases has been sig-

nificantly minimized by the use of sterilized human blood and nonhuman mammal blood in this exercise. However, use the same precautions you would if you were handling fresh and poten-

tially contaminated human blood. Your instructor will determine whether to use animal blood (from nonhuman mammals), sterilized blood, or synthetic blood. In any of these cases, follow strict procedures for handling potentially pathogenic material.

1. Wear protective gloves and goggles during the procedures.
2. Do not eat or drink in lab.
3. If you have an open wound, do not participate in this exercise or make sure the wound is *securely* covered.
4. Your instructor may elect to have you use your blood. Due to the potential for disease transmission, such as AIDS or hepatitis in fresh blood samples, *make sure you keep away from other students' blood and keep them away from your blood.*
5. Do not participate in this part of the exercise if you have recently skipped a meal or if you are not well.

6. Place all disposable material in the biohazard bag.
7. Place all used lancets in the sharps container and all glassware to be reused in a 10% bleach solution.
8. After you have finished the exercise, clean and disinfect the countertops with a 10% bleach solution.

OBJECTIVES

At the end of this exercise you should be able to

1. discuss the composition of blood plasma;
2. distinguish among the various formed elements of blood;
3. determine the percent of each type of leukocyte in a differential white cell count;
4. describe the significance of an elevated level of a particular white blood cell and what it may indicate about a disease state or an allergic reaction.

MATERIALS

Prepared slides of human blood with Wright's or Giemsa stain

Colored pencils

Compound microscopes

Lab charts or illustrations showing the various blood cell types

Dropper bottle of Wright's stain

Large finger bowl or staining tray

Toothpicks

Clean microscope slides

Coverslips

Squeeze bottle of distilled water or phosphate buffer solution

Pasteur pipette and bulbs

Sterile cotton balls

384   **LABORATORY 29** Blood

Adhesive bandages

Alcohol swabs

Sterile, disposable lancets

Goggles

Latex gloves

Roll of paper towels

Hand counter

Biohazard bag or container

Container with 10% bleach

Sharps container

PROCEDURE

Plasma

Plasma is the fluid portion of blood and is over 90% water by volume. The remainder mostly consists of proteins, such as albumins, globulins, and fibrinogen. Albumins are produced by the liver and make up the majority of the plasma proteins. They transport solutes and buffer the plasma, which has a pH of about 7.4. Some globulins are made by the plasma cells and make up the next largest amount of proteins. Globulins have an important function for immunity (as antibodies) and they aid in solute transport and blood clotting. Fibrinogen is a clotting protein and this and other clotting factors are produced by the liver. Plasma also contains electrolytes (Na^+, K^+, and Cl^-), nutrients, hormones, and wastes.

Examination of Blood Cells

Your lab instructor will direct you to use a prepared slide of blood; fresh, nonhuman mammal blood; or your blood. If you are using a prepared slide of blood you can move to the section entitled "Microscopic Examination of Blood Cells." If you are to make a smear, read the following directions.

Preparing a Fresh Blood Smear

If you are using nonhuman mammal blood, wear latex gloves and withdraw a small amount of blood with a clean Pasteur pipette. Place a drop of blood on a clean microscope slide; then proceed to step 8 in the following procedure.

Withdrawal of Your Blood

If you are using your blood make sure you follow the safety precautions as discussed at the beginning of the exercise. Obtain the following materials: a clean, sterile lancet; an alcohol swab; an adhesive bandage; rubber gloves; sterile cotton balls; two clean microscope slides; and a paper towel.

1. Arrange the materials on the paper towel in front of you on the countertop.
2. Warm your hands with water or by rubbing them to increase blood flow to the fingers.
3. Clean the end of the donor finger with the alcohol swab, let it dry momentarily, and let the hand from which you will withdraw blood hang by your side for a few moments to collect blood in the fingertips. You will be puncturing the pad of your fingertip (where the fingerprints are located lateral to the center of the finger).
4. Peel back the covering of the lancet and hold on to the *blunt* end as you withdraw it from the package. Do not touch the sharp end or lay the lancet on the table before puncturing your finger.
5. Prick your finger quickly and wipe away the first drop of blood that forms with a sterile cotton ball. Throw the lancet in the sharps container. Never reuse the lancet or set it down on the table!
6. Place the second drop of blood from your finger on the microscope slide about 2 cm away from one of the ends of the slide (see figure 29.1) and place another cotton ball on your finger.
7. Put an adhesive bandage on your finger.

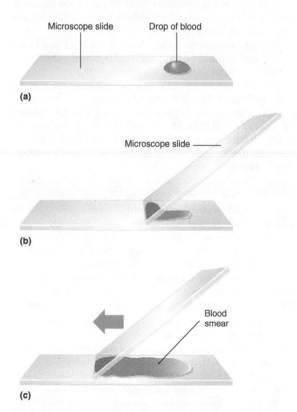

FIGURE 29.1 Making a Blood Smear (a) Placement of blood on slides; (b) touching glass slide to front of blood drop; (c) spreading blood across slide.

8. Whether you are using nonhuman blood or your blood, use another clean slide to spread the blood by touching the drop with the edge of the slide and pull the blood across the slide (see figure 29.1). This should produce a smooth, thin smear of blood. Let the blood smear dry completely.

9. After the slide is dry, place it in a large finger bowl elevated on toothpicks or on a staining tray.

10. Cover the blood smear with several drops of Wright's stain from a dropper bottle. Let the stain remain on the slide for 1 to 2 minutes.

11. After this time add water or a prepared phosphate buffer solution to the slide. You can rock the slide gently with gloved hands or blow on it to stir the stain and water. A metallic green material should come to the surface of the slide. Let the slide remain covered with stain and water for 4 minutes.

12. Wash the slide gently with distilled water until the material is light pink and then stand it on edge to dry. You may also stain blood using an alternate stain (Giemsa stain), following your lab instructor's procedure.

Place all blood-contaminated disposable material in the biohazard container. Place the slide used to spread the blood in the 10% bleach solution and place the lancets in the sharps container if you haven't done so already. Once the slide is completely dry it can be examined under the high-power or oil-immersion lens of your microscope.

Microscopic Examination of Blood Cells
Overview

As you examine the blood slide you should refer to figures 29.2 through 29.4. You will have to look at many blood cells to see all the cells included in this exercise.

Erythrocytes

Examine a slide of blood stained with either Wright's or Giemsa stain. Erythrocytes are the most common cells you will find on the slide. There are about 5 million erythrocytes per cubic millimeter. They do not have a nucleus but appear as pink, biconcave disks (like a donut with the hole partially filled in). This shape increases surface area and provides greater oxygen-carrying capabilities. Erythrocytes contain the pigment **hemoglobin,** which carries oxygen.

Erythrocytes are about 7.5 μm in diameter, on average, and have a life span of about 120 days, after which time they are broken down by the spleen or liver. The iron portion of the hemoglobin is used by the bone marrow to make more hemoglobin, the proteins are broken down to amino acids and reabsorbed for general use by the body, and the heme is metabolized to bilirubin in the liver and secreted as part of the bile. Compare what you see under the microscope to figure 29.2.

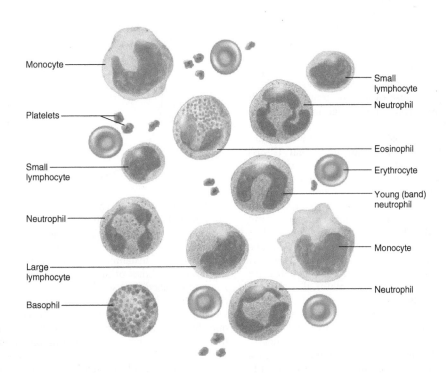

Monocyte

Platelets

Small lymphocyte

Neutrophil

Large lymphocyte

Basophil

Small lymphocyte

Neutrophil

Eosinophil

Erythrocyte

Young (band) neutrophil

Monocyte

Neutrophil

FIGURE 29.2 **Formed Elements of Blood**

Platelets

There are about 150,000 to 350,000 platelets per cubic millimeter of blood. **Platelets,** or **thrombocytes,** are small fragments of **megakaryocytes** involved in clotting. Examine the slide for small, purple fragments that may be single or clustered and compare them to the platelets in figure 29.2.

Leukocytes

There are far fewer leukocytes in the blood than erythrocytes. The number of leukocytes in a healthy adult is about 7,000 cells per cubic millimeter, with a range of 4,300 to 10,800 cells per cubic millimeter of blood. Leukocytes are formed in bone marrow and lymphoid tissue. The life span of a leukocyte varies from a few hours to several years. Many are capable of ameboid movement as they squeeze between cells of the vascular endothelium (a process termed *diapedesis*), engulfing foreign particles or cellular debris.

Leukocytes, or white blood cells, can be divided into two groups, **granular** and **agranular leukocytes.** Examine the slide under high power or oil immersion and identify the different leukocytes as presented in the following sections. Leukocytes have two major types of responses to immune reactions. One of these is **innate immunity,** which refers to a person having a reaction to microorganisms and foreign substances without prior exposure. Another kind of response is **adaptive immunity,** in which exposure to specific antigens initiates an immune reaction. Leukocytes have specific receptors and secrete specific antibodies for specific antigens.

Granular Leukocytes   Granular leukocytes (granulocytes) are so named because they have granules in their cytoplasm. The three types of granular leukocytes are neutrophils, eosinophils, and basophils.

Neutrophils are the most common of all leukocytes. They are also known as polymorphonuclear (PMN) leukocytes due to the variable shape of their nuclei (which are lobed, not round). Neutrophils typically have a half-life in the blood of about 6 hours and have ameboid capabilities. They squeeze between adjacent endothelial cells that make up blood capillaries and move into the interstitial spaces of tissues, where they engulf foreign particles or cellular debris. They move into connective tissue, where they typically live for an additional 1 to 4 days. Neutrophils move toward infection sites and destroy foreign material. They are the major phagocytic leukocyte. The granules of neutrophils absorb very little stain so their granules are light pink to light purple. Mature neutrophils can be distinguished from other leukocytes by their typically two- to five-lobed nucleus. They are about one and a half times the size of erythrocytes. Examine your slide

for neutrophils, compare them to figure 29.3, and draw one in the following space.

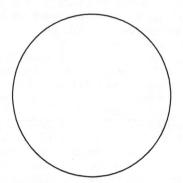

Eosinophils typically have a two-lobed nucleus with pink-orange granules in the cytoplasm. The term **eosinophil** means "eosin-loving" (eosin is an orange-pink stain and is picked up by the granules). They are about twice the size of erythrocytes. Eosinophils combat viruses and infections caused by multicellular pathogens, such as parasitic worms, and they are involved in allergic reactions. Compare figure 29.3 to your slide as you locate the eosinophils and draw one in the following space.

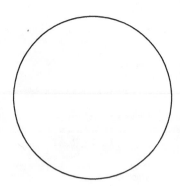

Basophils are rare. The granules stain very dark (blue-purple), and sometimes the nucleus is obscured because of the dark-staining granules. The nucleus is S-shaped and the cell is about twice the size of erythrocytes. Basophils contain the vasodilator histamine, which increases blood flow to the tissues. In times of infection it is beneficial to have an increase in blood flow so that phagocytic cells or antibodies can reach the infection site. Basophils also contain heparin, which is an anticoagulant. It keeps the blood from clotting too quickly. Clots decrease the effectiveness of combating infection as they can seal off the site from the immune reaction. They are involved in inflammatory and allergic reactions. You may have to look at 200 to 300 leukocytes before finding a basophil. Compare the basophil in your slide to figure 29.3 and draw one in the following space.

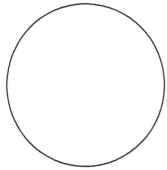

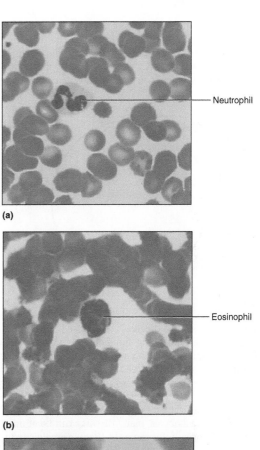

(a)

Agranular Leukocytes Agranular leukocytes are so named because they lack cytoplasmic granules. The nuclei are not lobed but may be dented or kidney bean–shaped. There are two types of agranular leukocytes, lymphocytes and monocytes.

Lymphocytes have a large, unlobed nucleus that usually has a flattened or dented area. The cytoplasm is clear and may appear as a blue halo around the purple nucleus. There are many types of lymphocytes. Two of them are the **B cells** and **T cells.** These cells cannot normally be distinguished from one another in standard histological preparations (for example, Wright's stain), and they are considered lymphocytes in this exercise. Both B cells and T cells arise from fetal bone marrow. The **B cells** probably mature in the fetal liver and spleen and in the bone marrow of adults. B cell lymphocytes become **plasma cells** when activated and make **antibodies.** Plasma cells provide **antibody-mediated immunity** (plasma cells secrete antibodies that travel in the blood plasma).

T cells mature in the thymus and provide **cell-mediated immunity.** In cell-mediated immunity the cells (not antibodies in the blood plasma) move close to and destroy some types of bacteria or virus-infected cells. T cells also attack tumors and transplanted tissues. Most of the T cells are found in the lymph nodes, thymus, and spleen. They enter the bloodstream via the lymphatics. **Natural killer (NK) cells** are lymphocytes that attack bacteria, transplanted cells, and cancer cells. Compare your slide to figure 29.4 for lymphocytes and draw one in the following space.

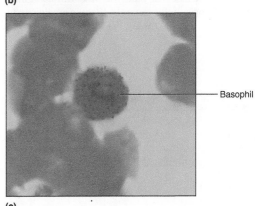

(b)

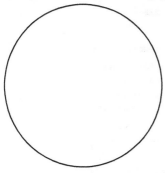

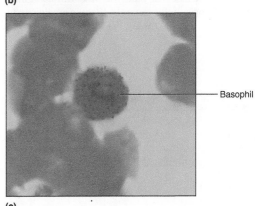

(c)

FIGURE 29.3 **Granular Leukocytes** (a) Neutrophil (1,000×); (b) eosinophil (1,000×); (c) basophil (1,500×).

Monocytes are large and have a kidney bean–shaped or horseshoe-shaped nucleus. They are about three times the size of erythrocytes and are activated by T cells. Monocytes are important in that they are major phagocytic cells, and they are important in presenting foreign antigens to T lymphocytes. Monocytes move into tissues from the blood and become **macrophages.** Locate the large cells on your slide, compare them to figure 29.4, and draw one in the following space. You can review the formed elements in table 29.1.

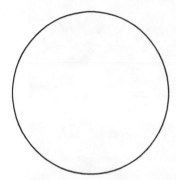

Differential Leukocyte Count

Rapid and inexpensive diagnosis of disease is a goal of modern health care. Narrowing the field of potential disease states is frequently done with a differential leukocyte count. For example, if a patient comes to the hospital with a fever, it could be due to many things, including viral infection, reactions to medications, metabolic disorders, and vascular disease. By taking a small sample of blood and examining the percentages of leukocytes, many diseases can be eliminated from the diagnosis. If, for example, there is an elevated lymphocyte count it may mean that there is a severe viral

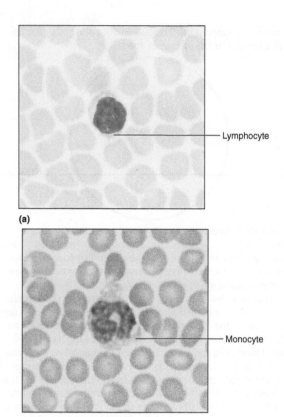

(a)

(b)

FIGURE 29.4 **Agranular Leukocytes (1,000×)**
(a) Lymphocyte; (b) monocyte.

TABLE 29.1	Summary of Formed Elements in Blood			
	Size	**Number**	**Characteristics**	
Erythrocytes	7.5 μm	5 million/mm³	Live 120 days on average No nucleus	
Platelets	2–4 μm	130,000–360,000/mm³	Cell fragments	
Leukocytes		7,000/mm³	Nucleus present	
Granular leukocytes				
Neutrophils	9–12 μm	60–70% of leukocytes	Three- to five-lobed nucleus granules indistinct	
Eosinophils	10–14 μm	2–4% of leukocytes	Two-lobed nucleus Orange granules	
Basophil	8–10 μm	0.5–1% of leukocytes	S-shaped nucleus Large, dark granules	
Agranular leukocytes				
Lymphocytes	5–17 μm	25–33% of leukocytes	Nucleus appearing dented Thin rim of cytoplasm in some	
Monocytes	12–15 μm	3–8% of leukocytes	Large, kidney-shaped nucleus	

infection in the body. It could also mean that there is an autoimmune disease or cancer in the lymph system, but it helps to direct the health-care provider to look for answers in certain areas and not in others. In this part of the exercise you examine a blood smear and count leukocytes to determine their percentages. Once you have determined the percentages, compare your values with the standard values to see if they are within normal limits. Changes in the relative percentages of leukocytes may indicate a type of disease.

Neutrophils represent about 60–70% of leukocytes. They increase in number in appendicitis or other acute bacterial infections.

Eosinophils represent about 2–4% of leukocytes. Eosinophils increase in number during allergic reactions and parasitic infections (for example, trichinosis).

Basophils represent about 0.5–1% of leukocytes. They increase in number during allergies and radiation.

Lymphocytes make up 25–33% of leukocytes. These cells increase in times of viral infection, such as infectious mononucleosis, and antibody-antigen reactions.

Monocytes make up about 3–8% of leukocytes. They increase in times of chronic infections, such as tuberculosis.

1. Use a hand counter and count 100 leukocytes. Look into the microscope and methodically record the different types of leukocytes seen.
2. You should record how many of each type are found and keep track of the overall number with the use of a hand counter until 100 cells are counted.
3. Scan the slide in a systematic way, so that you don't count any cell twice. One method is illustrated in figure 29.5. Tally your results in the following spaces.

Neutrophils: _____

FIGURE 29.5 **Counting Leukocytes**

Eosinophils: _____

Basophils: _____

Lymphocytes: _____

Monocytes: _____

Leukopenia is a decrease in the number of circulating leukocytes in the blood. Common causes are radiation therapy, chemotherapy, and some medications. **Leukemia** is an increase in the number of leukocytes. Even though the leukocytes are abundant, these cells are often immature or deformed and they do not function normally.

Fill in the following chart with what you know about the formed elements. Read all the information given before filling in the chart.

Clean Up Make sure the lab is clean after you finish. If you used immersion oil on the microscope make sure the objective lenses are wiped clean (use clean lens paper only!). Place any slide with fresh blood on it or any material contaminated with bodily fluid in the bleach solution. Place all gloves or contaminated paper towels in the biohazard container. All sharps material (broken slides or coverslips, lancets, etc.) should be placed in the sharps container. Clean the counters with a towel and a 10% bleach solution.

Characteristics of Formed Elements

Formed Element	Granules (If Present)	Shape of Nucleus (If Present)	Cause for Increase
Erythrocyte	No granules	No nucleus	_____
_____	Not obvious	_____	Mononucleosis
_____	Orange-staining	_____	Parasitic infections
_____	_____	Two- to five-lobed	_____
_____	Not obvious	Kidney-bean	_____
Basophil	_____	_____	_____

Notes

REVIEW SECTION ■■connect

|ANATOMY & PHYSIOLOGY

EXERCISE

29

Blood

Name _____ *Date* _____

Lab Section _____ *Time* _____

Review Questions

1. Formed elements have three main components. What are they?

2. What is the most common plasma protein?

3. What is another name for a platelet?

4. Which is the most common blood cell?

5. What is another name for a leukocyte?

6. What leukocyte is most numerous in a normal blood smear?

7. How many erythrocytes are normally found per cubic millimeter of blood?

8. What is an average number of leukocytes found per cubic millimeter of blood?

9. B cells and T cells belong to what class of agranular leukocytes?

392   **REVIEW 29** Blood

10. How does a differential leukocyte count aid in medical diagnosis?

11. In counting 100 leukocytes you are accurately able to distinguish 15 basophils. Is this a normal number for the white blood cell count, and what possible health implications can you draw from this?

12. What is the function of platelets?

13. Label the formed elements in the following illustration.

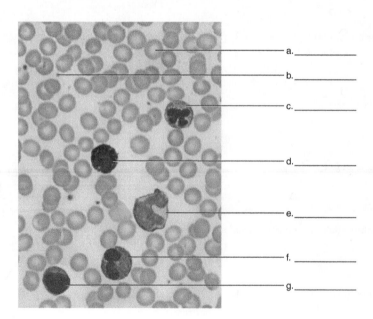

a. _____

b. _____

c. _____

d. _____

e. _____

f. _____

g. _____

LABORATORY

Structure of the Heart

INTRODUCTION

In this exercise you study the structure of the heart, which is covered in the Saladin text in chapter 19, "The Circulatory System: The Heart." The heart is located deep in the thorax between the lungs in a region known as the **mediastinum.** The mediastinum contains the heart, the membranes surrounding the heart (the **pericardium**), and other structures, such as the esophagus and descending aorta. The mediastinum is located between the sternum, lungs, and thoracic vertebrae. Vessels that return blood to the heart are called **veins,** and those that carry blood from the heart are called **arteries.**

If you were to open the chest cavity, the first structure you would see is the **pericardial sac (parietal**

pericardium). The pericardial sac encloses the heart and has two layers: a tough, outer connective tissue sheath called the fibrous layer and an inner layer called the serous layer. Deep to the pericardial sac is the **pericardial cavity,** which contains a small amount of **serous fluid.** This fluid reduces the friction between the outer surface of the heart and the pericardial sac. The heart wall has an outer layer known as the **epicardium,** or **visceral pericardium.** Locate these pericardial layers in figure 31.1.

In this exercise, you examine models of the heart, preserved sheep and human hearts, if available. As you look at the preserved material try to see how the structure of the heart relates to its function.

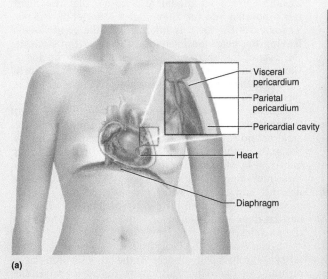

(a)

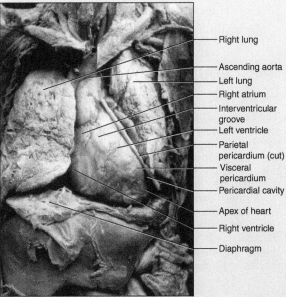

Right lung
Ascending aorta
Left lung
Right atrium
Interventricular groove
Left ventricle
Parietal pericardium (cut)
Visceral pericardium
Pericardial cavity
Apex of heart
Right ventricle
Diaphragm

(b)

Visceral pericardium
Parietal pericardium
Pericardial cavity
Heart
Diaphragm

FIGURE 31.1 **Heart in Thoracic Cavity and Heart Coverings**
(a) Coronal section; (b) photograph of cadaver.

OBJECTIVES

At the end of this exercise you should be able to

1. list the three layers of the heart wall;
2. describe the position of the heart in the thoracic cavity;
3. describe the significant surface features of the heart;
4. describe the internal anatomy of the heart;
5. find and name the anatomical features on models of the heart and in the sheep heart;
6. describe the blood flow through the heart and the function of the internal parts of the heart;
7. discuss the functioning of the atrioventricular valves and the semilunar valves and their role in circulating blood through the heart.

MATERIALS

Models and charts of the heart

Preserved sheep hearts

Preserved human hearts (if available)

Blunt probes (mall probes)

Dissection pans

Razor blades or scalpels

Sharps container

Disposable gloves

Waste container

Microscopes

Prepared slides of cardiac muscle

Fresh or thawed sheep heart

Clamp (hemostat) or string

PROCEDURE

Heart Wall

The heart wall is composed of three major layers. The outermost layer is the **epicardium,** or **visceral pericardium,** composed of epithelial and connective tissue. The middle layer is the **myocardium** and is the thickest of the three layers. It is mostly made of **cardiac muscle.** You may wish to review the slides of involuntary cardiac muscle and note the intercalated discs, branching fibers, and fine striations of cardiac tissue (as described in Laboratory Exercise 6). The cardiac muscle is arranged spirally around the heart, and this arrangement provides a more efficient wringing motion to the heart. The inner layer of the heart wall is

known as the **endocardium,** a membrane consisting of endothelium (simple squamous epithelium) and connective tissue.

 Caution!   Be careful when handling preserved materials. Ask your instructor for the proper procedure for working with preserving fluid and for handling and disposal of the specimen. Do not dispose of animal material in the sinks. Place it in an appropriate waste container.

It is best to examine heart models *before* dissecting a sheep heart unless your instructor directs you to do otherwise. Heart models are color coordinated and labeled to make the structures easier to locate.

Examination of the Heart Model
Overview

The heart is a four-chambered pump with two superior atria (AY-tree-uh) and two inferior ventricles. Blood enters the heart in the right atrium (see figure 31.2) and flows into the right ventricle. Once the blood is in the right ventricle the contraction of the ventricular wall sends the blood to the lungs. The blood is oxygenated in the lungs and returns to the heart by entering the left atrium. Blood moves from the left atrium to the left ventricle and is then pumped to the rest of the body.

Exterior of the Heart

Examine the heart model and notice that the heart has a pointed end, or **apex,** and a blunt end, or **base.** The apex of the heart is inferior, and the great vessels leaving the heart are located at the base (therefore, in the case of the heart, the base is superior to the apex). Compare the model to figure 31.2 and see how the **aorta** curves to the left in an anterior view of the heart and is posterior to the **pulmonary trunk.**

Locate the anterior features of the heart. The heart is composed of two large, inferior ventricles and two smaller and superior atria. The **left ventricle** extends to the apex of the heart and is delineated from the right ventricle by the **interventricular groove,** or sulcus. In this interventricular groove are some of the **coronary arteries** and **cardiac veins,** discussed later. The left ventricle is larger than the right ventricle. Note the two earlike flaps on the anterior, superior atria. These are the **auricles.**

If you examine the heart from the posterior side you will see the atria more clearly. At the junction of the right atrium and the right ventricle is the **atrioventricular**

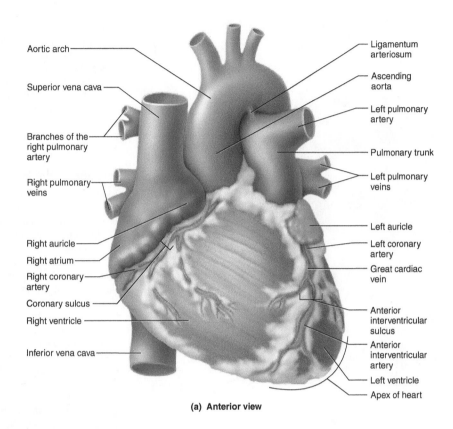

Aortic arch

Superior vena cava

Branches of the
right pulmonary
artery

Right pulmonary
veins

Right auricle

Right atrium

Right coronary
artery

Coronary sulcus

Right ventricle

Inferior vena cava

Ligamentum
arteriosum

Ascending
aorta

Left pulmonary
artery

Pulmonary trunk

Left pulmonary
veins

Left auricle

Left coronary
artery

Great cardiac
vein

Anterior
interventricular
sulcus

Anterior
interventricular
artery

Left ventricle

Apex of heart

(a) Anterior view

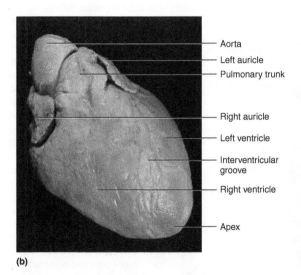

Aorta

Left auricle

Pulmonary trunk

Right auricle

Left ventricle

Interventricular
groove

Right ventricle

Apex

(b)

FIGURE 31.2 **Surface Anatomy of the Heart, Anterior View**
(a) Diagram; (b) photograph.

sulcus, or groove. The **coronary sinus,** a large venous space that carries blood from the cardiac veins to the right atrium, is located in this sulcus. Locate the **superior vena cava** and the **inferior vena cava,** two vessels that also return blood to the right atrium. Locate the **pulmonary veins,** which carry blood from the lungs to the left atrium. Compare the heart model to figure 31.3.

The major vessels of the heart are illustrated in figures 31.2, 31.3, and 31.4. Locate the **pulmonary trunk, pulmonary arteries, ligamentum arteriosum** (between the pulmonary trunk and aortic arch), **ascending aorta, pulmonary veins, superior vena cava, inferior vena cava, coronary arteries,** and **cardiac veins.**

The heart tissue is nourished by coronary arteries. The **left coronary artery** arises from the ascending aorta (see figure 31.4) and then branches into the **anterior interventricular artery** and the **circumflex artery.** The **right coronary artery** also arises from the ascending aorta and branches to form the **posterior interventricular artery** and the **right marginal artery.** These major arteries of the heart supply blood to the myocardium. On the return flow from the heart muscle the **great cardiac vein** follows the depression of

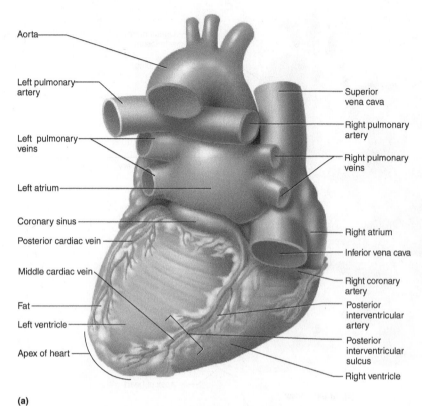

Aorta

Left pulmonary artery

Left pulmonary veins

Left atrium

Coronary sinus

Posterior cardiac vein

Middle cardiac vein

Fat

Left ventricle

Apex of heart

Superior vena cava

Right pulmonary artery

Right pulmonary veins

Right atrium

Inferior vena cava

Right coronary artery

Posterior interventricular artery

Posterior interventricular sulcus

Right ventricle

(a)

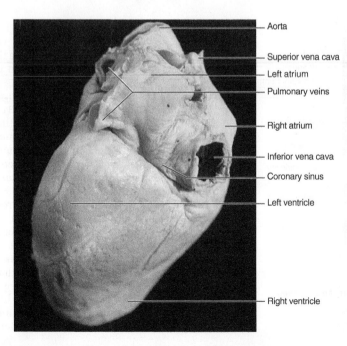

Aorta

Superior vena cava

Left atrium

Pulmonary veins

Right atrium

Inferior vena cava

Coronary sinus

Left ventricle

Right ventricle

(b)

FIGURE 31.3 **Surface Anatomy of the Heart, Posterior View** (a) Diagram; (b) photograph.

the interventricular groove and the atrioventricular groove to the coronary sinus. On the right side of the heart the **small cardiac vein** leads to the coronary sinus, which empties into the right atrium. Locate these vessels on the external surface of the model of the heart and compare them to figures 31.2, 31.3, and 31.4.

Interior of the Heart

Examine a model of the interior of the heart and locate the right and left ventricles. The muscular wall of the **right ventricle** is much thinner walled than the **left ventricle.** This is because blood from the right ventricle is pumped a short distance to the lungs while blood in the left ventricle is pumped more extensively through the body. The ventricles are separated by the **interventricular septum,** which forms a wall between the two ventricular chambers. Compare the model to figure 31.5.

Examine the **right atrium** and note how thin the wall is compared to the ventricles. The walls of the atria are thin because blood in the atria has to flow only a short distance to the ventricles. Examine the medial wall of the atrium, known as the **interatrial septum,** and locate a thin, oval depression in the atrial wall. This depression is the **fossa ovalis.** In fetal hearts this is the site of the **foramen ovale** (for-AYE-men o-VAL-eh), but closure of the foramen usually occurs just after birth. Note the extensive **pectinate** (PEK-tin-ate) **muscles** on the wall of the atrium. These provide additional strength to the atrial wall. Blood in the superior vena cava, the inferior vena cava, and the coronary sinus returns to the right atrium. Examine the features of the right atrium in figures 31.5 and 31.6.

The blood from the right atrium flows into the right ventricle. Now examine the valve between the right atrium and right ventricle. This is the **right atrioventricular valve,** or **tricuspid valve,** and it prevents return of blood from the right ventricle into

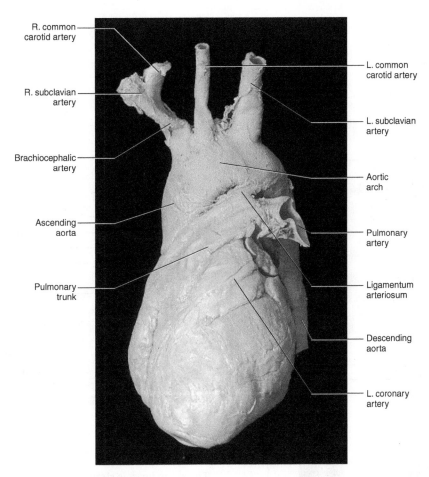

R. common carotid artery

R. subclavian artery

Brachiocephalic artery

Ascending aorta

Pulmonary trunk

L. common carotid artery

L. subclavian artery

Aortic arch

Pulmonary artery

Ligamentum arteriosum

Descending aorta

L. coronary artery

FIGURE 31.4 **Vessels of the Heart, Anterior View**

the right atrium during ventricular contraction. Examine the valve for three flat sheets of tissue. These are the three cusps of the tricuspid valve. The tricuspid valve has thin, threadlike attachments called **chordae tendineae** (COR-day TEN-din-ee). These tough cords are attached to larger **papillary muscles,** extensions from the wall of the ventricle. The right ventricle wall has small extensions called **trabeculae carneae** (trah-BEC-you-lee CAR-nee-ee). The blood from the right ventricle flows into the pulmonary trunk toward the lungs.

Locate the **pulmonary semilunar valve.** It appears as three small cusps between the right ventricle and the pulmonary trunk and keeps blood from flowing in reverse from the pulmonary trunk into the right ventricle during ventricular relaxation. Examine the details of the right ventricle in models in the lab and in figure 31.5.

Blood from the pulmonary trunk flows into the pulmonary arteries prior to entering the lungs. Blood in the lungs releases carbon dioxide and picks up oxygen. The **pulmonary veins** carry oxygenated blood from the lungs into the **left atrium.** These vessels are located in the superior, posterior portion of the left atrium. Blood from the left atrium flows into the left ventricle. Locate the two large cusps of the bicuspid valve between the left atrium and left ventricle. The **bicuspid valve** is also known as the **mitral valve,** or **left atrioventricular valve.** It also has attached chordae tendineae and papillary muscles, which you should locate in the models in the lab. Note the thickness of the left ventricle wall compared to the wall of the right ventricle. Compare the left side of the heart to figure 31.5.

The **aortic semilunar valve** is located at the junction of the left ventricle and the ascending aorta. It has the same basic structure and general function as the pulmonary semilunar valve in that it prevents the flow of blood from the aorta into the left ventricle. Blood from the left ventricle moves into the aorta and subsequently to the rest of the body.

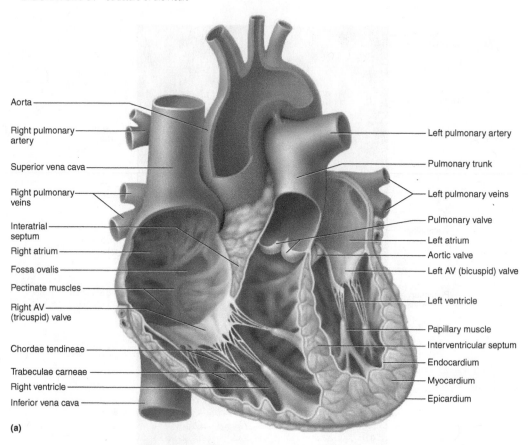

Aorta

Right pulmonary artery

Superior vena cava

Right pulmonary veins

Interatrial septum

Right atrium

Fossa ovalis

Pectinate muscles

Right AV (tricuspid) valve

Chordae tendineae

Trabeculae carneae

Right ventricle

Inferior vena cava

Left pulmonary artery

Pulmonary trunk

Left pulmonary veins

Pulmonary valve

Left atrium

Aortic valve

Left AV (bicuspid) valve

Left ventricle

Papillary muscle

Interventricular septum

Endocardium

Myocardium

Epicardium

(a)

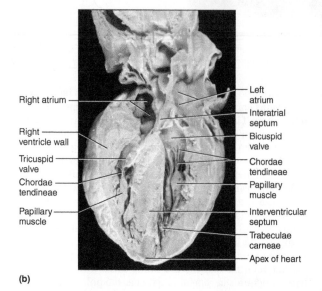

Right atrium

Right ventricle wall

Tricuspid valve

Chordae tendineae

Papillary muscle

Left atrium

Interatrial septum

Bicuspid valve

Chordae tendineae

Papillary muscle

Interventricular septum

Trabeculae carneae

Apex of heart

(b)

FIGURE 31.5 **Heart, Frontal Section** (a) Diagram; (b) photograph.

Dissection of the Sheep Heart

The sheep heart is similar to the human heart and usually is readily available as a dissection specimen. Dissection of anatomical material is valuable in that you can examine structures seen more accurately in preserved material than in models. Also, the preserved material has greater flexibility and is easily manipulated. There are some differences between sheep hearts and human hearts, especially in the position of the superior and inferior venae cavae. In sheep these are called the anterior and posterior venae cavae, but we refer to them using the human terminology.

If your sheep heart has not been dissected, then you will need to open the heart. If your sheep or other mammalian heart has been previously dissected, then you can skip the next two paragraphs.

Place the heart under running water for a few moments to rinse off the preserving fluid. Examine the external features of the heart, as seen in figure 31.7. The sheep heart may still be in the pericardial sac. If this is the case, remove the sac before proceeding. Note the fat layer on the heart. The amount of fat on the human or sheep heart is variable. Locate the **left ventricle,** the **right ventricle,** the **interventricular groove (sulcus),** the **right atrium,** and the **left atrium.** Note the **auricles** that extend

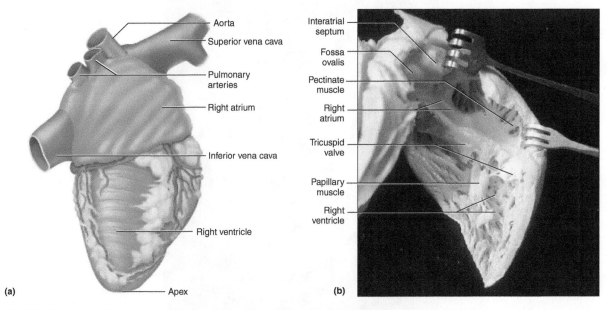

FIGURE 31.6 **Right Side of the Heart** (a) Diagram of surface view; (b) photograph of interior view.

from the anterior surface of the atria. Carefully remove the adipose tissue from the major vessels of the heart.

Using a sharp scalpel or razor blade, make an incision along the right *side* of the heart (lateral side) from the apex of the heart to the lateral side of the right atrium. If you are unsure about how to proceed during any part of the dissection, ask your instructor for directions. Make another long cut from the lateral side of the left atrium through the lateral side of the left ventricle. You will make a coronal section of the heart if you cut through the **interventricular septum.** Once you have opened the heart, compare the structures of the sheep heart to figure 31.8.

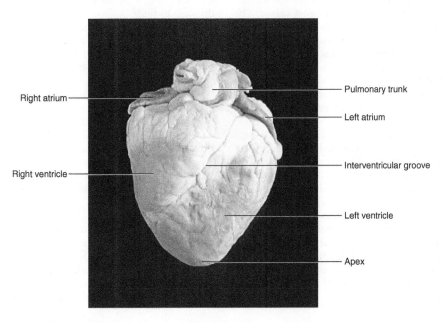

FIGURE 31.7 **Sheep Heart, Anterior View**

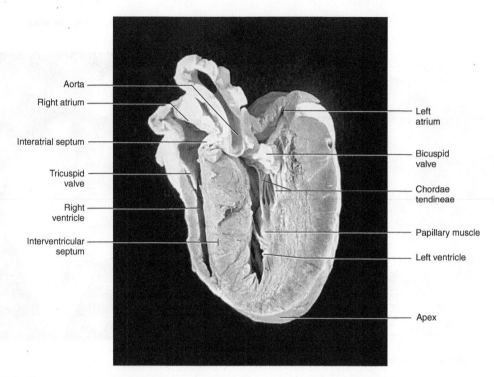

Aorta

Right atrium

Interatrial septum

Tricuspid valve

Right ventricle

Interventricular septum

Left atrium

Bicuspid valve

Chordae tendineae

Papillary muscle

Left ventricle

Apex

FIGURE 31.8 Sheep Heart, Coronal Section

You can locate the vessels of the heart by gently inserting a blunt metal probe into the vessels and determining which chamber the vessel goes to or comes from. Place the heart in anatomical position and insert the probe into the large, anterior vessel that exits toward the specimen's left side. Be careful and do not tear the heart valves. The blunt end of the probe should enter the right ventricle. This vessel is the **pulmonary trunk.** The pulmonary trunk may still have the **pulmonary arteries** attached. Locate the large vessel directly behind the pulmonary trunk (see figures 31.7 and 31.8). This is the **ascending aorta.** If the vessels are cut farther away from the heart, you can see the **aortic arch.** Insert the probe into this vessel and into the **left ventricle.**

Turn the heart to the posterior surface and locate the **superior (anterior) vena cava** and **inferior (posterior) vena cava.** Insert the probe into the superior and inferior vena cavae, pushing the probe into the **right atrium.** If you find only one large opening in the atrium, you may have cut through either the superior or inferior vena cava during your initial dissection. The probe can be felt through the wall more easily here than in a ventricle because the atrial walls are thinner than those of the ventricles. On the left side the **pulmonary veins** may appear as four separate veins, or you may see a large hole on each side of the **left atrium** if the vessels were cut close to the atrial wall. Locate the same structures in

the sheep heart as you found on the model and compare them to figure 31.9.

Cut into the right atrium and use your blunt probe to locate the opening of the **coronary sinus** in the posterior, inferior portion of the atrium. It is small and somewhat difficult to find.

Examine the opening between the right atrium and the right ventricle to locate the **tricuspid valve.** You may have dissected through one of the cusps as you opened the heart. Locate the major features of the **right ventricle.** Find the **chordae tendineae** and the **papillary muscles.** You can find the **pulmonary trunk** by inserting a blunt probe into the superior portion of the right ventricle. Make an incision in the pulmonary trunk near the right ventricle to expose the three thin cusps of the **pulmonary semilunar valve.** Note how the cusps press against the wall of the pulmonary trunk when the probe is pushed against them in a superior direction. These cusps close when blood begins to flow back into the right ventricle as the ventricle relaxes.

Locate the **left atrium, bicuspid valve,** and **left ventricle.** In the left ventricle you should find the papillary muscles, chordae tendineae, and **trabeculae carneae.** You can find the aorta and aortic semilunar valve by inserting a blunt probe toward the superior end of the left ventricle toward the middle of the heart.

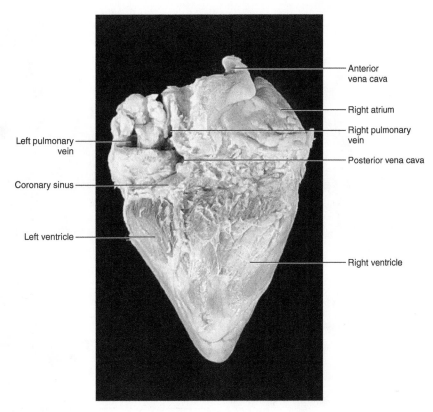

- Anterior vena cava
- Right atrium
- Right pulmonary vein
- Posterior vena cava
- Right ventricle

Left pulmonary vein

Coronary sinus

Left ventricle

FIGURE 31.9 Sheep Heart, Posterior View

Clean Up When you have finished your study of the sheep heart make sure you clean your dissection equipment with soap and water and dry it. Be careful with sharp blades. Place the sheep heart either back in the preserving fluid or in the appropriate waste container as directed by your instructor.

Heart Valves

The semilunar valves and atrioventricular valves prevent the backflow of blood. Your instructor may demonstrate the procedure, or you can do it yourself by using a fresh or thawed sheep heart. Flush any remaining blood from the heart before you locate the valves.

Make an incision into the right atrium, exposing the **tricuspid valve.** Pour water into the right ventricle and notice how the water flows past the tricuspid valve and into the right ventricle. Clamp off the pulmonary trunk or tie it with string to prevent blood from flowing out of the pulmonary trunk. *Gently* squeeze the right ventricle and notice how the right atrioventricular valve closes and prevents blood from backing up into the right atrium.

What is the adaptive value for the closing of atrioventricular valves?

Cut the **pulmonary trunk** close to the right ventricle and slowly pour water into it as if you were trying to fill the right ventricle. The **pulmonary semilunar valve** should fill with water and close the entrance of the right ventricle, preventing backflow. This normally occurs as the right ventricle begins diastole. Compare these valve closures to figure 31.10.

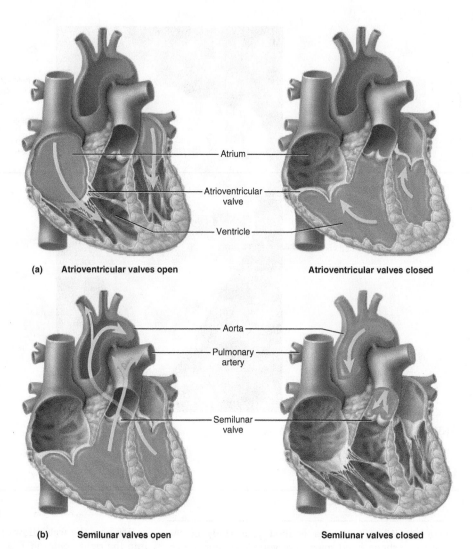

(a)   **Atrioventricular valves open**

Atrioventricular valves closed

Atrium

Atrioventricular valve

Ventricle

Aorta

Pulmonary artery

Semilunar valve

(b)   **Semilunar valves open**

Semilunar valves closed

FIGURE 31.10 **Closure of the Heart Valves** (a) Atrioventricular valve; (b) semilunar valve.

REVIEW SECTION ■connect
|ANATOMY & PHYSIOLOGY

Structure of the Heart

Name _____   *Date* _____

Lab Section _____   *Time* _____

Review Questions

1. The heart is located between the lungs in an area known as the:

2. Name the outer (superficial) layer of the pericardium.

3. What is the innermost layer of the heart wall called?

4. Name the depression between the two ventricles seen on the anterior surface of the heart.

5. Are auricles extensions of the atria or the ventricles?

6. What three vessels take blood to the right atrium?

7. Where do the great cardiac vein and the small cardiac vein take blood?

8. Is the apex of the heart superior or inferior to other parts of the heart?

9. What blood vessels nourish the heart tissue?

10. What structure separates the left atrium from the right atrium?

11. The bicuspid valve is located between what two chambers of the heart?

414   **REVIEW 31**   Structure of the Heart

12. What is the function of the aortic semilunar valve?

13. Name the structure found between the atrioventricular valve and the papillary muscle.

14. What is another name for the tricuspid valve?

15. What is the cell type that makes up most of the myocardium?

16. The walls of the left ventricle are thicker than those of the right ventricle. What explanation can you give for this?

17. How does cardiac muscle resemble skeletal muscle?

18. In terms of function, how is cardiac muscle different from skeletal muscle?

19. What is the function of the semilunar valves?

20. Trace the flow of blood through the heart.

21. Label the following illustration using the terms provided.

    right atrium

    right ventricle (wall)

    left ventricle (wall)

    tricuspid valve

    aorta

    left atrium

    apex

    chordae tendineae

    interventricular septum

    bicuspid valve

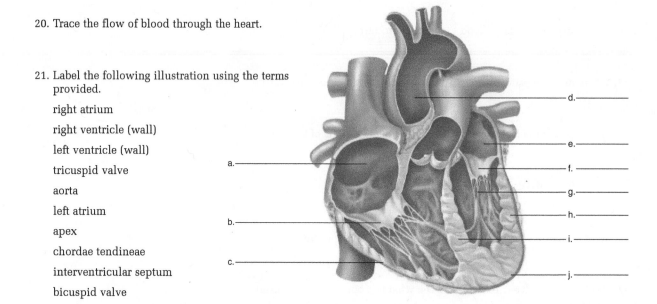

42

LABORATORY

Anatomy of the Digestive System

INTRODUCTION

The digestive system can be divided into two major parts, the **alimentary canal** and the **accessory organs.** The alimentary canal is a long tube that runs from the mouth to the anus and comes into contact with food or the breakdown products of digestion. Some of the organs of the alimentary canal are the esophagus, stomach, intestines, rectum, and anus. The accessory organs are important in that they secrete many important substances necessary for digestion, yet these organs do not come into direct contact with food. Examples of accessory organs are the salivary glands, liver, gallbladder, and pancreas.

The functions of the digestive system are many and include ingestion of food, physical breakdown of food, chemical breakdown of food, food storage, water absorption, vitamin synthesis, absorption of digested material, and elimination of indigestible material. These topics are covered in the Saladin text in chapter 25, "The Digestive System."

In this exercise you examine the anatomy of the digestive system in both human and cat, correlating the structure of the digestive organs with their functions.

OBJECTIVES

At the end of this exercise you should be able to

1. list, in sequence, the major organs of the alimentary canal;
2. describe the basic function of the accessory digestive organs;
3. note the specific anatomical features of each major digestive organ;
4. describe the layers of the wall of the gastrointestinal tract;
5. describe the major functions of the stomach and small and large intestines;
6. distinguish among different regions of the alimentary canal by their histology.

MATERIALS

Models, charts, or illustrations of the digestive system

Mirror

Materials for Cat Dissection

Cats

Dissection trays

Scalpels or razor blades

Protective gloves

Waste container

Skull, human teeth, or cast of teeth

Cadaver (if available)

Microscopes

Microscope slides

Esophagus

Stomach

Small intestine

Large intestine

Liver

PROCEDURE

Overview of the Digestive Organs

Begin this exercise by examining a torso model or charts in the lab and compare them to figure 42.1. Locate the major digestive organs and place a check mark in the appropriate space.

_____ Mouth

_____ Teeth

_____ Pharynx

_____ Esophagus

534   **LABORATORY 42** Anatomy of the Digestive System

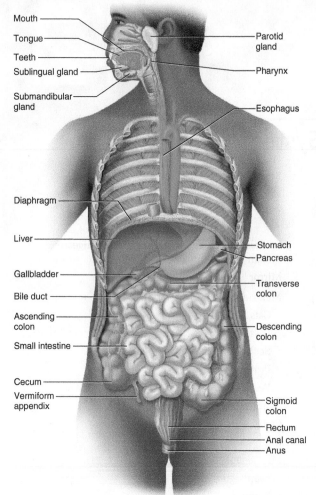

FIGURE 42.1 **Overview of the Digestive System**

_____ Stomach
_____ Small intestine
_____ Large intestine (colon)
    _____ Ascending colon
    _____ Transverse colon
    _____ Descending colon
    _____ Sigmoid colon
    _____ Rectum
_____ Anal canal
_____ Anus
_____ Liver
_____ Vermiform appendix

_____ Pancreas
_____ Gallbladder
_____ Salivary glands

Alimentary Canal

Begin your study of the alimentary canal with the mouth. Examine a midsagittal section of the head, as represented in figure 42.2, and locate the major anatomical features.

Mouth

At the beginning of the alimentary canal is the **mouth.** The opening of the mouth is surrounded by **lips,** or **labia.** The **labial frenulum** is a membranous structure that keeps the lip adhered to the gums, or **gingivae.** The mouth is a space bordered in front by the lips, behind by the oropharynx, and on the sides by the inner wall of the cheeks. The hard and soft palates form the roof of the mouth, and the floor of the chin is the inferior border. The **hard palate** is composed of the palatine processes of the maxillae and palatine bones. The **soft palate** is composed of connective tissue and a mucous membrane. At the posterior portion of the mouth is the **uvula,** a small, grapelike structure suspended from the posterior edge of the soft palate. The uvula helps prevent food or liquid from moving into the nasal cavity during swallowing. The mouth is lined with **nonkeratinized stratified squamous epithelium,** which protects the underlying tissue from abrasion. The **tongue** is made of skeletal muscle. One of the major muscles of the tongue is the **genioglossus.** The tongue is important in speech, taste, the movement of food toward the teeth for chewing, and swallowing. The tongue acts as a piston to propel food

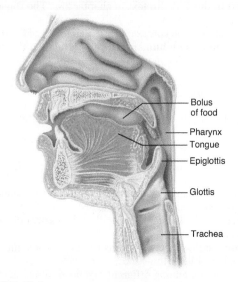

FIGURE 42.2 **Oral Cavity, Midsagittal Section**

to the **oropharynx,** the space behind the oral cavity. The tongue is held down to the floor of the mouth by a thin mucous membrane called the **lingual frenulum.** Use a mirror to examine the three types of **papillae,** or raised areas, on the tongue. These are **fungiform, filiform,** and **vallate** (circumvallate) papillae. Papillae increase the frictional surface of the tongue. **Taste buds** occur on the tongue along the sides of the papillae. The sense of taste is covered in Laboratory Exercise 25.

The mouth is important in digestion for the physical breakdown of food. This process is driven by powerful muscles called the **muscles of mastication.** The **masseter** and the **temporalis muscles** are involved in the closing of the jaws, and the **pterygoid muscles** are important in the sideways grinding action of the molar and premolar teeth.

Teeth   Examine models of teeth, dental casts, or real teeth on display in the lab and compare them to figure 42.3. A tooth consists of a **crown, neck,** and **root.** The crown is the exposed part of the tooth; the neck is a constricted portion of the tooth that normally occurs at the surface of the gingivae; and the root is embedded in the jaw. Examine a model or an illustration of a longitudinal section of a tooth and find the outer **enamel,** an extremely hard material. Inside this layer is the **dentine,** which is made of bonelike

material. The innermost portion of the tooth consists of the **pulp cavity,** which leads to the **root canal,** a passageway for nerves and blood vessels into the tooth. The nerves and blood vessels enter the tooth through the **apical foramen** at the tip of the root of the tooth. The teeth occur in depressions in the mandible or maxilla called **alveolar sockets** and are anchored into the bone by the periodontal ligament.

There are four different types of teeth in the adult mouth:

- **Incisors** are flat, bladelike front teeth that nip food. There are eight incisors in the adult mouth.
- **Canines,** or **cuspids,** are the pointed teeth just lateral to the incisors that function in shearing food. There are four canines in the adult, and they can be identified as the teeth with just one cusp, or point.
- **Premolars,** or **bicuspids,** are lateral to the canines; they grind food. There are typically eight premolars in adults, and they can be identified by their two cusps.
- **Molars** are found closest to the oropharynx. These grind food, and there are 12 molar teeth in the adult mouth (including the wisdom teeth). Molars typically have three to five cusps.

Examine a human skull or dental cast and identify the characteristics of the four different types of teeth (figure 42.4).

Humans have two sets of teeth: the **deciduous,** or "milk," **teeth** appear first, and these are replaced by the **permanent teeth.** There are 20 deciduous teeth. In children there are no deciduous premolar teeth, and there are only 8 deciduous molar teeth. In adults there are 8 premolar teeth and 12 molar teeth. Compare figure 42.4, the adult pattern, to figure 42.5, the deciduous teeth.

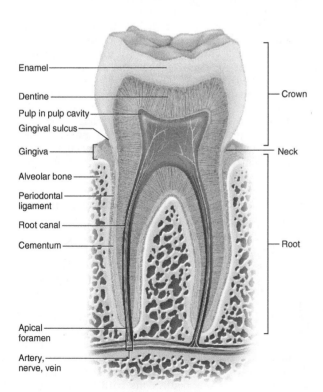

FIGURE 42.3 **Tooth, Longitudinal Section**

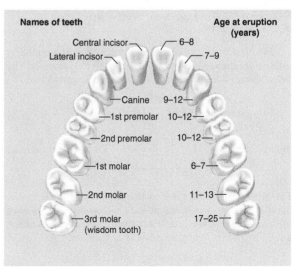

FIGURE 42.4 **Upper Teeth of an Adult**

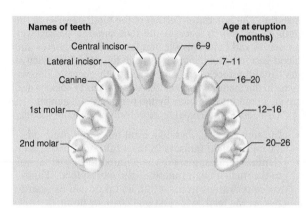

(a)

(b)

FIGURE 42.5 **Deciduous Teeth** (a) Upper teeth; (b) replacement of teeth.

Frequently, the pattern of tooth structure is represented by a **dental formula,** which describes the teeth by quadrants. The dental formula for the deciduous teeth is illustrated here.

I = incisor, C = canine,
P = premolar, and M = molar.

Deciduous teeth (20 total)

dental formula	I	C	P	M	
	2	1	0	2	One side (quadrant) Top
	2	1	0	2	Bottom

The upper numbers refer to the number of teeth in the maxilla on one side of the head. The lower numbers refer to the number of teeth in the mandible on one side of the head. The adult dental formula is as follows:

Adult (permanent) teeth (32 total)

I	C	P	M
2	1	2	3
2	1	2	3

Oropharynx

The **oropharynx** is the space behind the mouth that serves as a common passageway for air, food, and liquid. Above the oropharynx is the **nasopharynx,** which leads to the nasal cavity, and below the oropharynx is the **laryngopharynx,** which leads to the larynx and the esophagus. The oropharynx is composed of nonkeratinized stratified squamous epithelium. Muscles around the wall of the oropharynx are the **pharyngeal constrictor muscles** and are involved in swallowing. Food is moved by the tongue to the region of the pharynx, where it is propelled into the esophagus. Locate the oropharynx and the esophagus in figure 42.2.

Esophagus

The esophagus conducts food and liquid from the oropharynx, through the diaphragm, and into the stomach. Normally, the esophagus is a closed tube that begins at about the level of the sixth cervical vertebra. As a lump of food, or **bolus,** enters the esophagus, skeletal muscle begins to move it toward the stomach. The middle portion of the esophagus is composed of both **skeletal** and **smooth muscle,** while the lower portion of the esophagus is made of smooth muscle. In the lower region of the esophagus, the smooth muscle contracts, moving the bolus by a process known as **peristalsis.** The esophagus has an inner epithelial lining of **stratified squamous epithelium** and an outer connective tissue layer called the **adventitia.** Identify the four layers of the esophagus—mucosa, submucosa, muscularis, and adventitia—under the microscope. The space inside the esophagus where food passes through is called the **lumen,** which continues through the gastrointestinal tract. The lower portion of the esophagus has an **esophageal (cardiac) sphincter,** which prevents the backflow of stomach acids. **Heartburn** occurs if the stomach contents pass through the esophageal sphincter and irritate the esophageal lining.

Abdominal Portions of the Alimentary Canal

The inner structure of the body has been referred to as a "tube within a tube." The body wall forms the outer tube; the gastrointestinal tract, including the stomach, small intestine, and large intestine, forms the inner tube. Specialized serous membranes cover the various organs and line the inner wall of the **coelom** (body cavity). The membrane lining the outer surface of the gastrointestinal tract is called the **visceral peritoneum (serosa)** and it continues as a double-folded membrane called the **mesentery,** which attaches the tract to the back of the body wall. In between the linings of the mesentery are arteries, veins, nerves, and lymphatics. The mesentery is continuous with the membrane on the inner side of the body wall, where it is called the **parietal peritoneum.** Locate these three membranes in figure 42.6.

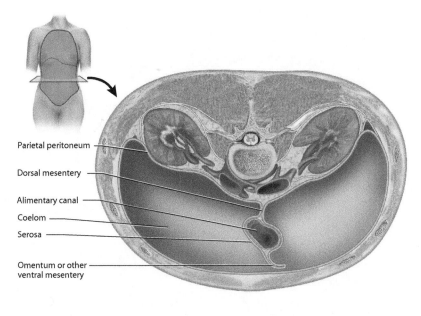

Parietal peritoneum

Dorsal mesentery

Alimentary canal

Coelom

Serosa

Omentum or other
ventral mesentery

Anterior

FIGURE 42.6 **Membranes of the Gastrointestinal Tract (Idealized Drawing)**

The gastrointestinal tract has a series of layers seen in microscopic sections. In general, the stomach, small intestine, and large intestine have the same layers from the lumen to the coelom. The innermost layer is the **mucosa,** which consists of a mucous membrane closest to the lumen, a connective tissue layer called the **lamina propria,** and an outer, muscular layer called the **muscularis mucosae.**

The next layer is called the **submucosa,** mostly made of connective tissue and containing numerous blood vessels. The next layer is the **muscularis (or muscularis externa),** typically made of two or three layers of smooth muscle. The muscularis propels material through the gastrointestinal tract and mixes ingested material with digestive juices. The outermost layer is called the **serosa,** or **visceral peritoneum,** and this layer is closest to the coelom. Examine a microscope slide of the gastrointestinal tract (small intestine) and locate these three membranes in figure 42.7.

Stomach

The **stomach** is located on the left side of the body and receives its contents from the esophagus. The food that enters the stomach is stored and mixed with the enzyme pepsin and hydrochloric acid to form a soupy material called **chyme.** The stomach can have a pH as low as 1 or 2. Chyme remains in the stomach as the acids denature proteins and pepsin reduces proteins to shorter

fragments. The acid of the stomach also has an antibacterial action, as most microbes do not grow well in conditions of low pH.

Examine a model of the stomach or charts in the lab and compare them to figure 42.8. Locate the upper portion of the stomach called the **cardia,** or **cardiac region.** A part of the cardia extends superiorly as a domed section called the **fundic region,** or **fundus.** The main part of the stomach is called the **body** and the terminal portion of the stomach, closest to the small intestine, is called the **pyloric region.** The pyloric region has an expanded area called the **antrum** and a narrowed region called the **pyloric canal.** The pylorus leads to the duodenum, and this opening is controlled by the **pyloric sphincter.** The left side of the stomach is arched and forms the **greater curvature,** while the right side of the stomach is a smaller arch, forming the **lesser curvature.** The inner surface of the stomach has a series of folds called **rugae,** which allow for expansion of the stomach. The contents are held in the stomach by two sphincters. The proximal **esophageal sphincter** prevents stomach contents from moving into the esophagus. The distal pyloric sphincter prevents the premature release of stomach contents into the small intestine. Locate the pyloric sphincter at the terminal portion of the stomach.

Stomach Histology   Examine a prepared slide of stomach. Identify the four primary layers: **mucosa, submucosa,**

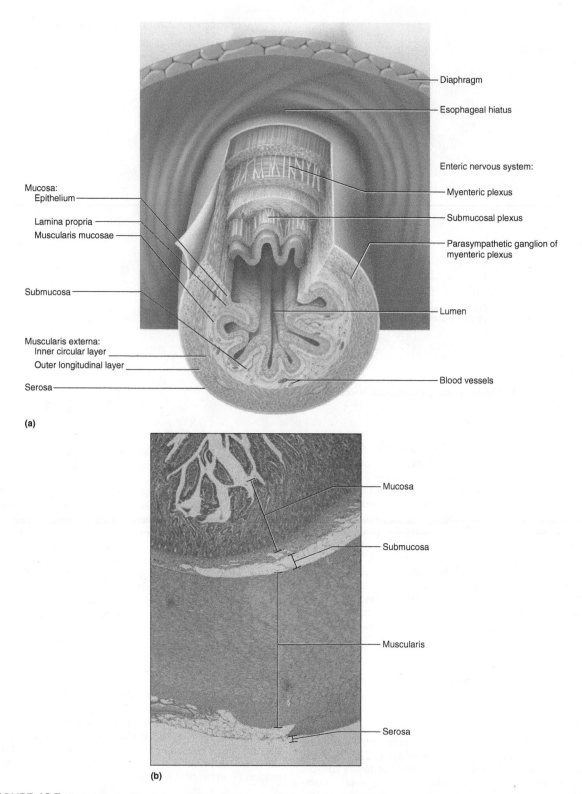

Diaphragm

Esophageal hiatus

Enteric nervous system:

Myenteric plexus

Submucosal plexus

Parasympathetic ganglion of myenteric plexus

Lumen

Blood vessels

Mucosa:
Epithelium

Lamina propria
Muscularis mucosae

Submucosa

Muscularis externa:
Inner circular layer
Outer longitudinal layer

Serosa

(a)

Mucosa

Submucosa

Muscularis

Serosa

(b)

FIGURE 42.7 **Gastrointestinal Tract, Cross Section** (a) Diagram; (b) photomicrograph (100×).

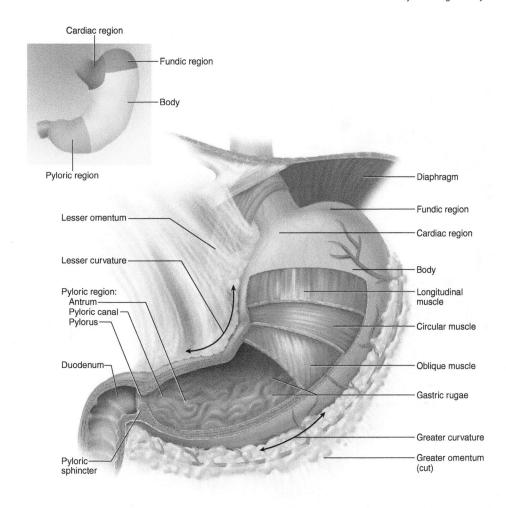

FIGURE 42.8 **Gross Anatomy of the Stomach**

muscularis, and **serosa.** Notice how the mucosa in the prepared slide has a series of indentations. These depressions are **gastric pits,** at the bottom of which are the **gastric glands.** These occur in the inner lining of the stomach. The mucous membrane is composed predominantly of **simple columnar epithelium. Surface mucous cells** occur in the membrane and secrete **mucus,** which protects the stomach lining from erosion by stomach acid and the **proteolytic** (protein-digesting) enzyme **pepsin.** Other specialized cells that you might find in the mucosa are **chief cells,** which secrete **pepsinogen** (the inactive state of pepsin). Chief cells contain blue-staining granules in some prepared slides. Other cells are **parietal cells,** which secrete HCl. They typically contain orange-staining granules. When pepsinogen comes into contact with HCl it is activated as pepsin.

Deeper to the mucous membrane locate the **lamina propria,** usually lighter in color. The **muscularis mucosae** is even farther away from the lumen and moves the mucous membrane. The **submucosa** is the next layer and is typically lighter in color in prepared slides.

The next layer of the stomach is the **muscularis.** In some parts of the stomach there are three layers of the muscularis—an **inner oblique layer,** a **middle circular layer,** and an **outer longitudinal layer.** The muscularis moves chyme from the stomach through the pyloric sphincter and into the small intestine. It also mixes the chyme.

The outermost layer is the **serosa,** and it is composed of a thin layer of connective tissue and **simple squamous epithelium.** Locate these structures and compare them to figure 42.9.

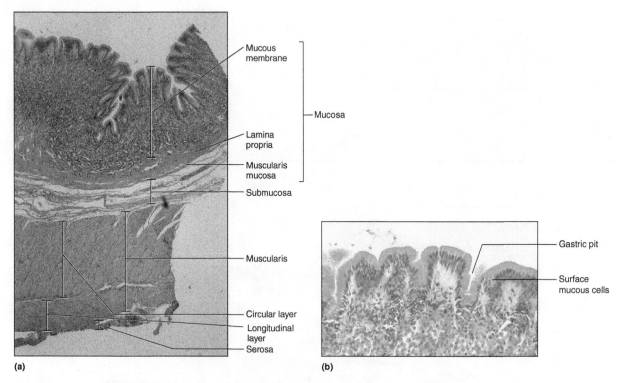

(a)

(b)

FIGURE 42.9 **Histology of the Stomach** (a) Overview (40×); (b) mucosa (100×).

Small Intestine

The **small intestine**, named because it is small in diameter, is approximately 5 m (17 ft) long. It is typically 3 to 4 cm (1.5 in.) in diameter when empty. Movement through the small intestine occurs by peristalsis, smooth muscle contraction. The primary function of the small intestine is nutrient absorption.

Locate the three major regions of the small intestine on a model or chart and compare them to figure 42.10. The first part of the small intestine is the **duodenum**, a C-shaped structure attached to the pyloric region of the stomach. The duodenum is partly retroperitoneal in that a portion of it is posterior to the parietal peritoneum. The duodenum is approximately 25 cm (10 in.) long. It receives fluid from both the **pancreas** and the **gallbladder.** The gallbladder releases **bile,** which emulsifies lipids, into the duodenum. The lipids break into smaller droplets, which increase the surface area for digestion. The bile is transported to the duodenum by the common bile duct. The pancreas secretes many digestive enzymes (proteases, amylases, and lipases) and bicarbonate, which neutralize the stomach acids. These are secreted into the duodenum by the **pancreatic duct.** The pancreatic duct often joins

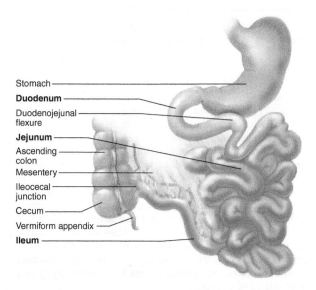

FIGURE 42.10 **Gross Anatomy of the Small Intestine**

with the common bile duct to form the **hepatopancreatic ampulla** (ampulla of Vater).

The second portion of the small intestine is the **jejunum,** approximately 2 m (6.5 ft) in length. The junction between the jejunum and the duodenum is known as the **duodenojejunal flexure.** The terminal portion of the small intestine is the **ileum,** approximately 3 m (10 ft) in length. A closure between the small intestine and large intestine is called the **ileocecal valve.** This valve keeps material in the large intestine from reentering the small intestine. Locate the small intestine and associated structures in figure 42.10.

Histology of the Small Intestine

Villi distinguish the small intestine from both the stomach and the large intestine. Villi are fingerlike projections that increase the surface area of the mucosa. Each villus contains **blood vessels,** which transport sugars and amino acids from the intestine to the liver. In addition to this, the villi contain **lacteals,** which transport triglycerides as chylomicrons via lymphatics to the venous system. When seen with the naked eye, villi give the lining of the small intestine a velvety appearance. The inner lining of the small intestine consists of **simple columnar epithelium** with **goblet cells.** You can distinguish the three sections of the small intestine by noting that the duodenum has **duodenal (Brunner's) glands** in the submucosa. The jejunum and the ileum lack these glands. The ileum is distinguished by the presence of **aggregated lymph nodules,** or **Peyer's patches,** present in the submucosa. These lymph nodules contain lymphocytes, which are activated and protect the body from the bacterial flora in the lumen of the small intestine. Compare the prepared slides of the small intestine to figure 42.11.

Large Intestine

The **large intestine** is so named because it is large in diameter. The large intestine is approximately 7 cm (3 in.) in diameter and 1.4 m (4.5 ft) in length. The function of the large intestine is the absorption of water, some vitamins, and solutes and the formation of feces. The mucosa of the large intestine is made of **simple columnar epithelium** with a large number of **goblet cells.** There are no villi present, nor aggregated lymph nodules, yet the wall of the large intestine has solitary lymph nodules.

Look at a model or chart of the large intestine and note the major regions. Compare them to figure 42.12.

- **Cecum:** first part of the large intestine. The cecum is a pouchlike area that articulates with the small intestine at the level of the ileocecal valve.
- **Ascending colon:** found on the right side of the body. It becomes the transverse colon at the right colic (hepatic) flexure.
- **Transverse colon:** traverses the body from right to left. It leads to the descending colon at the left colic (splenic) flexure.

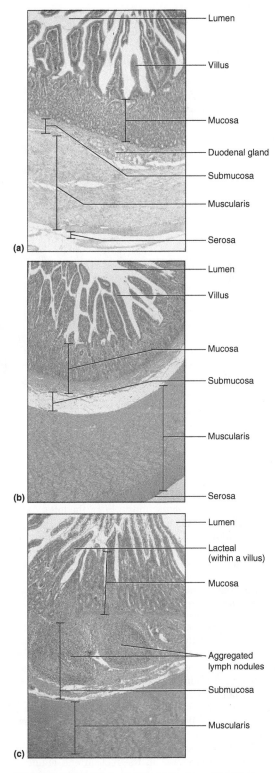

FIGURE 42.11 Three Sections of Small Intestine (40×)
(a) Duodenum; (b) jejunum; (c) ileum.

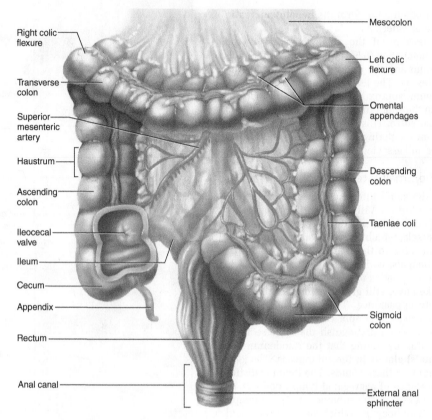

FIGURE 42.12 **Gross Anatomy of the Large Intestine**

- **Descending colon:** passes inferiorly on the left side of the body and joins with the sigmoid colon.
- **Sigmoid colon:** an S-shaped segment of the large intestine in the left inguinal region.
- **Rectum:** a straight section of colon in the pelvic cavity. The rectum has superficial veins in its wall called **hemorrhoidal veins.** These may enlarge and cause the uncomfortable condition known as **hemorrhoids.**

The large intestine has some unique structures. The longitudinal layer of the muscularis of the large intestine is not found as a continuous sheet but occurs along the length of the large intestine as three bands called **taeniae coli.** These muscles contract and form pouches or puckers in the intestinal tract called **haustra** (singular, *haustrum*). Another unique feature of the outer wall of the large intestine are fat lobules called **omental (epiploic) appendages.** Locate these structures in figure 42.12.

Fecal material passes through the large intestine by peristalsis and is stored in the rectum and sigmoid colon. **Defecation** occurs as **mass peristalsis** causes a bowel movement.

Histology of the Large Intestine Examine a prepared slide of the large intestine and compare it to figure 42.13. The large intestine is distinguished from the small intestine by the absence of villi and from the stomach by the presence of large numbers of goblet cells. Examine your slide for these characteristics.

Anal Canal

The **anal canal** is not part of the large intestine but is a short tube that leads to an external opening, the anus. Locate the anal canal in figure 42.12.

Accessory Organs
Salivary Glands

The **salivary glands,** located in the head, secrete **saliva** into the mouth. Saliva is a watery secretion that contains **mucus** (a protein lubricant) and **salivary amylase,** a starch-digesting enzyme. The average adult secretes about 1.5 liters of saliva per day.

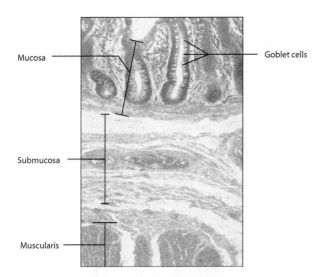

FIGURE 42.13 **Histology of the Large Intestine (100×)**

There are three pairs of salivary glands. The first of these, the **parotid glands,** are located just anterior to the ears. Each gland secretes saliva through a **parotid duct,** a tube that traverses the buccal (cheek) region and enters the mouth just posterior to the upper second molar. The second pair, the **submandibular glands,** are located just medial to the mandible on each side of the face. The submandibular glands secrete saliva into the mouth by a single duct on each side of the mouth inferior to the tongue. The third pair, the **sublingual glands,** are located inferior to the tongue, which open into the mouth by several ducts. Locate these salivary glands on a model of the head and in figure 42.14.

Vermiform Appendix

The **vermiform appendix** is about the size of your little finger and is located near the junction of the small and large intestines (at the region of the ileocecal valve). Locate the appendix on a torso model or chart in the lab and compare it to figure 42.15. The appendix is absent in the cat.

Omenta

The **lesser omentum** is an extension of the peritoneum that forms a double fold of tissue between the stomach and the liver. The **greater omentum** is a section of peritoneum that originates between the stomach and transverse colon and drapes over the intestines as a fatty apron. Locate the lesser and greater omenta in figure 42.16.

Liver

The **liver** is a complex organ with numerous functions; some are digestive but many are not. The liver processes digestive products from the vessels returning blood from

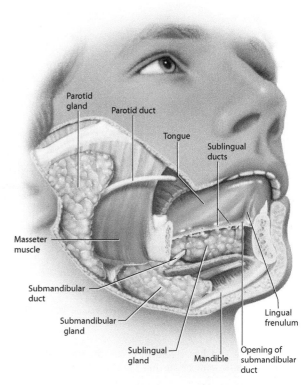

FIGURE 42.14 **Salivary Glands**

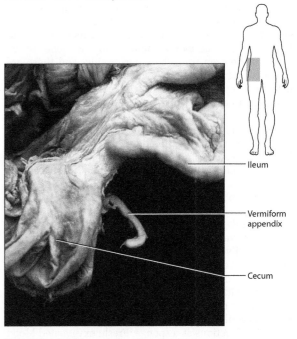

FIGURE 42.15 **Vermiform Appendix**

544   **LABORATORY 42** Anatomy of the Digestive System

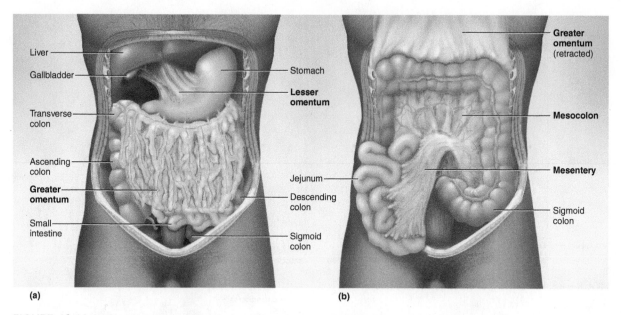

(a)

(b)

FIGURE 42.16 **Omenta, Mesentery, and Mesocolon** (a) Superficial view of greater omentum; (b) view of deeper layers.

the intestines and has a role in either moving nutrients into the bloodstream or storing them in the liver tissue. The liver also produces blood plasma proteins; detoxifies harmful material that has been produced by, or introduced into, the body; and produces bile.

Examine a model or chart of the liver and note its relatively large size. The liver is located on the right side of the body and is divided into four lobes, the **right, left, quadrate,** and **caudate lobes.** Only two lobes of the liver can be seen from the anterior side, and these are the large right lobe and the smaller left lobe. These two lobes are separated by a slip of mesentery called the falciform ligament, which suspends the liver from the diaphragm. In an inferior view of the liver all four lobes can be seen. The quadrate lobe is a small, rectangular lobe adjacent to the gallbladder, and the caudate lobe is at the posterior edge of the liver near the inferior vena cava. Locate the **gallbladder,** on the inferior aspect of the liver, and compare the gallbladder and liver structures to figure 42.17.

Liver Histology   Examine a prepared slide of liver tissue. Note the hexagonal structures in the specimen. These are known as **liver lobules.** Each lobule has a blood vessel in the middle called the **central vein.** Vessels that carry blood to the central vein are the liver **sinusoids,** and these are lined with a double row of cells called **hepatocytes.** Hepatocytes carry out the various functions of the liver as just described. The tissue of the liver is extremely vascular and functions as a sponge. Fresh, oxygenated blood

from the hepatic artery and deoxygenated blood from the hepatic portal vein mix in the liver. **Kupffer cells** are macrophages that occur throughout the liver tissue and function as phagocytic cells. Locate the lobules, central vein, sinusoids, bile ductule, and hepatocytes in a prepared slide, using figure 42.18 to aid you.

Pancreas

The **pancreas** is located inferior to the stomach and on the left side of the body. It has both endocrine and exocrine functions. The hormonal function of the pancreas is covered in Laboratory Exercise 28. The exocrine function of the pancreas is studied in Laboratory Exercise 43. The pancreas consists of a **tail,** found near the spleen; an elongated **body;** and a rounded **head,** located near the duodenum. Enzymes and buffers pass from the tissue of the pancreas into the **pancreatic duct** and then into the duodenum. Locate the pancreatic structures, as represented in figure 42.19.

Gallbladder

The **gallbladder** is located just inferior to the liver. The liver is the site of bile production, and the bile flows from the liver through **left** and **right hepatic ducts** to enter the **common hepatic duct.** Once in the common hepatic duct the bile flows into the **cystic duct** and then is stored in the gallbladder where it is concentrated. As the stomach begins to empty its contents into the duodenum the gallbladder constricts, and bile flows from

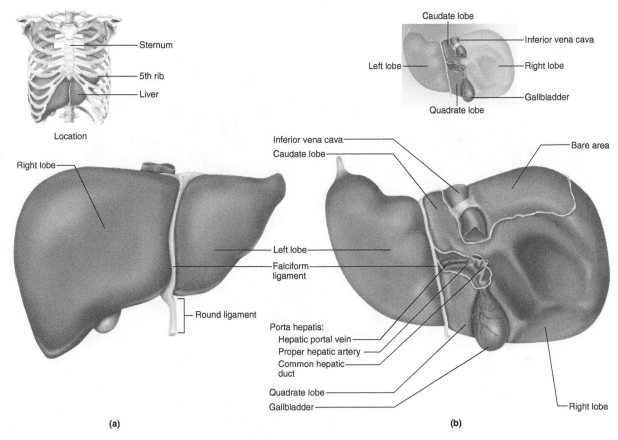

FIGURE 42.17 **Liver** (a) Anterior view; (b) inferior view (dorsal is at top of liver in diagram).

the gallbladder back into the cystic duct and into the **common bile duct,** which empties into the duodenum. Locate these structures on a model and compare them to figure 42.19.

Cat Dissection

Prepare for the dissection by obtaining a cat and dissection equipment. Remember to place all excess tissue in the appropriate waste container and not in a standard wastebasket or down the sink!

Begin your study of the digestive system of the cat by locating the large **salivary glands** around the face. You must first remove the skin from in front of the ear. If you have dissected the face for the musculature you may have already removed the **parotid gland,** a spongy, cream-colored pad anterior to the ear. You can also locate the **submandibular gland** as a pad of tissue slightly anterior to the angle of the mandible and lateral to the digastric muscle. The **sublingual gland** is just anterior

to the submandibular gland and is an elongated gland that parallels the mandible. Use figure 42.20 to help you locate these glands.

Dissection of the head of the cat should be done only if your instructor gives you permission to do so. To dissect the head you should first use a scalpel and make a cut in the midsagittal plane from the forehead of the cat to the region of the occipital bone. Cut through any overlying muscle in the cat. You should then use a small saw and gently cut through the cranial region of the skull, being careful to stay in the midsagittal plane. Once you make an initial cut through the dorsal side of the head, you should cut the mental symphysis of the cat, thus separating the mandible.

You can then use a long knife (or scalpel) to cut through the softer regions of the skull, brain, and tongue. Use a scalpel to cut through the floor of the oral cavity to the hyoid bone. It is best to use a scissors or small bone cutter to cut through the hyoid bone. This should allow you to open the head and examine the structures seen

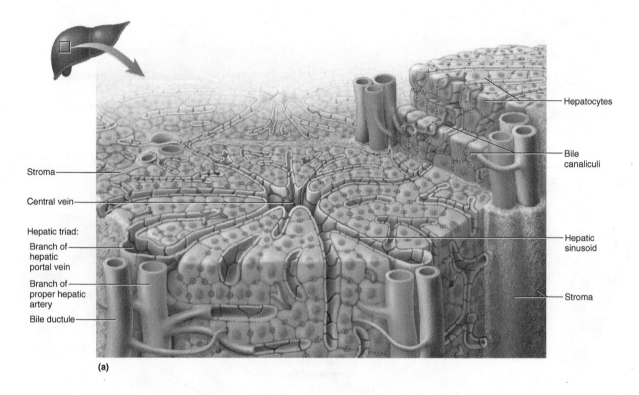

Hepatocytes

Bile canaliculi

Stroma

Central vein

Hepatic triad:
Branch of hepatic portal vein

Branch of proper hepatic artery

Bile ductule

Hepatic sinusoid

Stroma

(a)

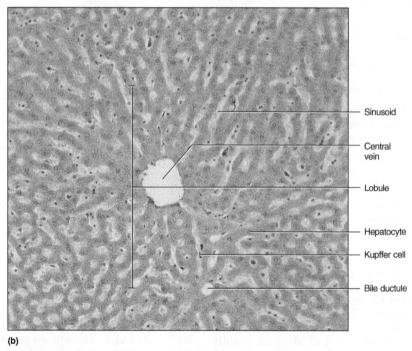

Sinusoid

Central vein

Lobule

Hepatocyte

Kupffer cell

Bile ductule

(b)

FIGURE 42.18 **Histology of the Liver** (a) Diagram; (b) photomicrograph (100×).

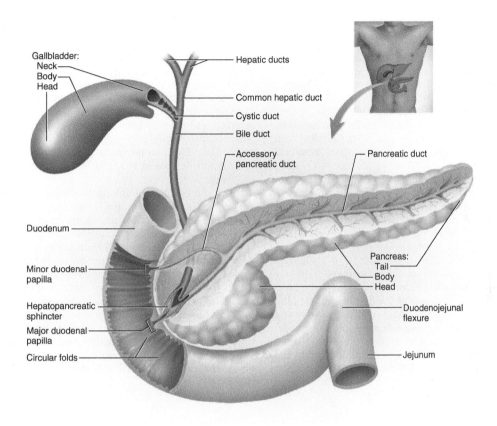

FIGURE 42.19 **Gallbladder, Pancreas, and Duodenum**

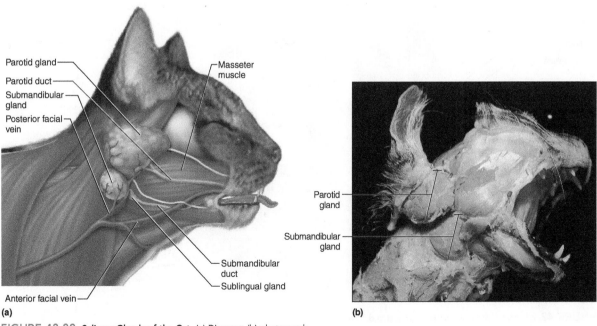

(a)   **(b)**

FIGURE 42.20 **Salivary Glands of the Cat** (a) Diagram; (b) photograph.

in a midsagittal section, as seen in figure 42.21. Locate the hard palate, tongue, oral cavity, and oropharynx. Note how the larynx in the cat is closer to the tongue than in humans.

Examine the **tongue** of the cat and note the numerous papillae on the dorsal surface. These are **filiform papillae.** They have both a digestive and a grooming function. You can lift up the tongue and examine the **lingual frenulum** on the ventral surface.

Look for the muscular tube of the esophagus by carefully lifting the trachea ventrally away from the neck. You should be able to insert your blunt dissection probe into the oral cavity and gently wiggle it into the esophagus. The tongue and esophagus are represented in figure 42.21.

Abdominal Organs

To get a better view of the abdominal organs it is best to cut the **diaphragm** away from the anterior body wall. Carefully cut the lateral edges of the diaphragm from the ribs. You should see a fatty drape of material covering the intestines. This is the **greater omentum.** Just caudal to the diaphragm note the dark brown, multilobed **liver.** In the middle of the liver is the green **gallbladder.** To the left of the liver (in reference to the cat) is the J-shaped

stomach. Lift the liver and locate the **lesser omentum,** a fold of tissue that connects the stomach to the liver. Locate these structures in figure 42.22.

Make an incision into the stomach and locate the folds known as rugae. Place a blunt probe inside the stomach and move it anteriorly. Notice how the esophageal sphincter makes it difficult to pass through the diaphragm. If you do move the probe into the esophagus you should be able to see it as you look anterior to the diaphragm.

The stomach has an anterior cardia, a domed fundus, greater and lesser curvatures, and a pyloric region. Cut into the pyloric region of the stomach and through the duodenum. Locate a tight sphincter muscle between the stomach and the duodenum. This is the pyloric sphincter. As you move into the duodenum you may have to scrape some of the chyme away from the wall of the small intestine to be able to see the fuzzy texture of the intestinal wall. This texture is due to the presence of villi. As in the human, the small intestine is composed of three regions, the duodenum, the jejunum, and a terminal ileum. Compare the stomach and small intestine to figure 42.22.

Elevate the greater omentum to see the pancreas, along the caudal side of the stomach. The pancreas

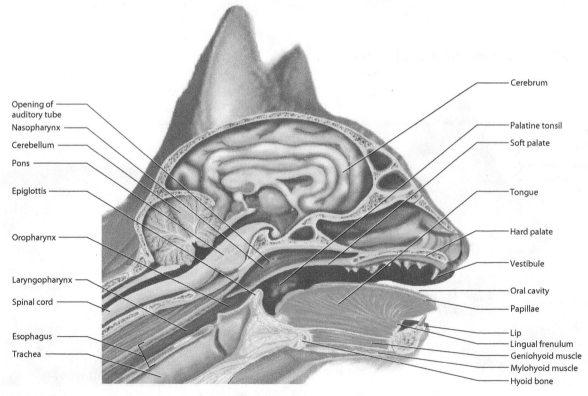

FIGURE 42.21 **Midsagittal Section of the Head and Neck of a Cat**

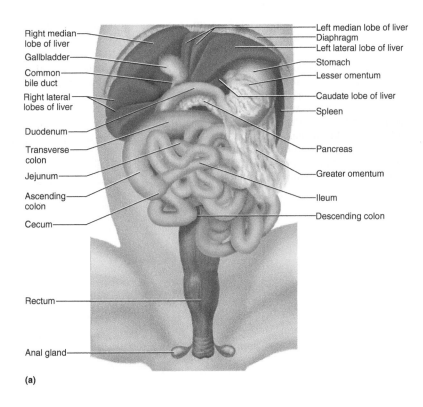

(a)

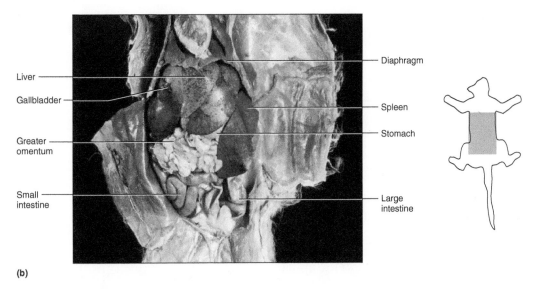

(b)

FIGURE 42.22 **Abdominal Organs of the Cat** (a) Diagram; (b) photograph.

appears granular and brown. The tail of the pancreas is near the spleen, a brown, elongated organ on the left side of the body.

The small intestine is an elongated, coiled tube about the diameter of a wooden pencil. Note the **mesentery,** which holds the small intestine to the posterior body wall near the vertebrae. The small intestine is extensive in the cat and rapidly expands into the large intestine. There is no vermiform appendix in the cat. In humans it is found at the ileocecal junction. The large intestine in the cat is a fairly short tube, with a diameter slightly larger than your thumb. The first part of the large intestine is a pouch called the cecum. The remainder of the large intestine can be further divided into the ascending, transverse, and descending colon and the rectum. Compare these to figure 42.22. Examine the **parietal peritoneum** along the inner surface of the body wall and the visceral peritoneum that envelops the intestines.

Clean Up When you are done with your dissection carefully place your cat back in the plastic bag.

REVIEW SECTION ▦ connect
|ANATOMY & PHYSIOLOGY

Anatomy of the Digestive System

Name _____   *Date* _____

Lab Section _____   *Time* _____

Review Questions

Matching

Match the terms on the left with those on the right. A term may be used more than once or not at all.

Set One

1. pancreas   a. jejunum

2. descending colon   b. pyloric region

3. part of the stomach closest to the small intestine   c. ileum

4. middle portion of the small intestine   d. alimentary canal

5. distal portion of the small intestine   e. accessory organ

Set Two

6. outer surface of the stomach   a. submucosa

7. layer adjacent to the lumen of intestine   b. serosa

8. cell type in the muscularis   c. mucosa

9. location of the villi   d. smooth muscle

10. What is semidigested food in the stomach called?

11. Where do you find lacteals in the digestive tract?

12. What membrane holds the tongue to the floor of the mouth?

13. What part of the tooth is found above the neck?

552   **REVIEW 42**   Anatomy of the Digestive System

14. What is the layer of a tooth superficial to the dentine?

15. What are the adult teeth directly posterior to the canine teeth called?

16. The segments or pouches of the large intestine have what particular name?

17. What are the names of the salivary glands anterior to the ear?

18. Where is the lesser omentum found?

19. Where does the cystic duct take bile for storage?

20. Stomach acidity is in the range of pH 1 to 2. How might this inhibit the growth of ingested bacteria?

21. Trace the flow of bile from the liver to the duodenum, listing all the structures that come into contact with the bile on its journey.

22. How does the large intestine differ from the small intestine in length?

23. How does the large intestine differ from the small intestine in diameter?

24. Name two functions of the pancreas.

25. Label the following illustration using the terms provided.

ascending colon	vermiform appendix	sigmoid colon
rectum	tongue	small intestine
mouth	duodenum	esophagus
stomach	parotid gland	liver

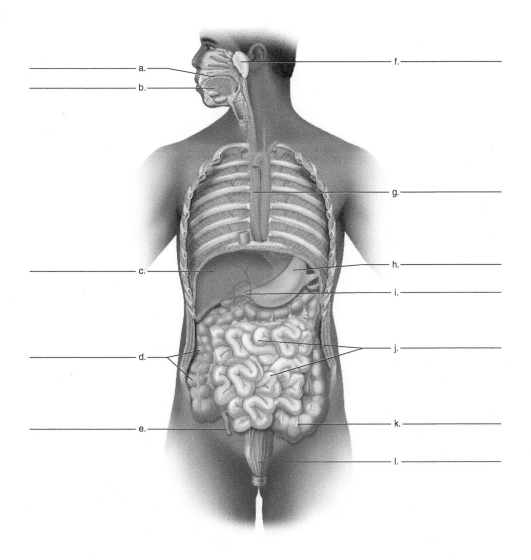

Notes

44

LABORATORY

Urinary System

INTRODUCTION

The organs of the urinary system consist of two kidneys, two ureters, a single urinary bladder, and a single urethra. The urinary system filters dissolved material from the blood, regulates electrolytes and fluid volume, concentrates and releases waste products, and reabsorbs metabolically important substances back into the circulatory system. **Filtration** occurs when one or more substances pass through a selectively permeable membrane while others do not. Filtration in the kidney involves both metabolic waste products (urea) and material beneficial to the body. Not all filtered material is desirable to have **excreted** from the body. Glucose and other materials, such as sodium and potassium ions, are **reabsorbed** from the kidney back into the circulatory system. The kidney **secretes** urea; some drugs; hydrogen and hydroxyl ions; and hormones, such as erythropoietin and the enzyme renin. Finally the kidneys excrete metabolic wastes, hydrogen ions, toxins, water, and salts. These topics are discussed in the Saladin text in chapter 23, "The Urinary System." In this exercise you examine the gross and microscopic anatomy of the urinary system, study the major organs as represented in humans, and dissect a mammal kidney if available.

OBJECTIVES

At the end of this exercise you should be able to

1. list the major organs of the urinary system;
2. describe the blood flow through the kidney;
3. describe the flow of filtrate through the kidney;
4. name the major parts of the nephron;
5. trace the flow of urine from the kidney to the exterior of the body;
6. distinguish between the parts of the nephron in histological sections;
7. compare male and female urinary anatomy.

MATERIALS

Models and charts of the urinary system

Models and illustrations of the kidney and nephron system

Microscopes

Microscope slides of kidney and bladder

Samples of renal calculi (if available)

Preserved specimens of sheep or other mammal kidney

Dissection Trays and Materials

Scalpels or razor blades

Forceps

Blunt (mall) probes

Latex gloves

Waste container

PROCEDURE

Overview

You can begin the study of the urinary system by locating its principal organs. Look at figure 44.1 and compare it to the material available in the lab. Find the **kidneys,** the **ureters,** the **urinary bladder,** and the **urethra.**

Kidneys

The kidneys are **retroperitoneal** (posterior to the parietal peritoneum) and are embedded in the **perirenal fat capsule.** The capsule cushions the kidneys, which are found mostly below the protection of the rib cage. The kidneys are located adjacent to the vertebral column

566 **LABORATORY 44** Urinary System

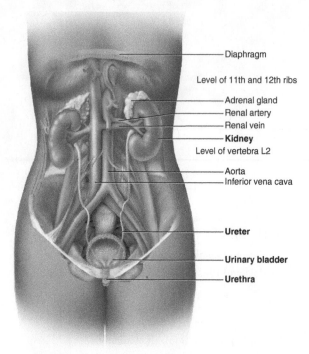

Diaphragm

Level of 11th and 12th ribs

Adrenal gland
Renal artery
Renal vein
Kidney
Level of vertebra L2

Aorta
Inferior vena cava

Ureter

Urinary bladder

Urethra

FIGURE 44.1 **Major Organs of the Urinary System**

about at the level of T12 to L3. The right kidney is slightly more inferior than the left.

1. Examine a model of the kidney and compare it to figure 44.2.
2. Locate the outer **fibrous capsule,** a tough connective tissue layer; the outer **cortex;** and the inner **medulla** of the kidney. The kidney has a depression on the medial side where the renal artery enters the kidney and the renal vein and the ureter exit the kidney. This depression is called the **hilum.**
3. Examine a coronal section of the kidney, and find the **renal (medullary) pyramids,** separated by the **renal columns.** Each renal pyramid ends in a blunt point called the **renal papilla** (see figure 44.2). Urine drips from many papillae toward the middle of the kidney.

   The urine drips into the **minor calyces** (singular, *calyx*), which enclose the renal papillae. Minor calyces are somewhat like funnels that collect fluid. Minor calyces lead to the **major calyces** and these, in turn, conduct urine into the large **renal pelvis.** The renal pelvis is found in the **renal sinus.** The renal pelvis is like a glove in a coat pocket. The pocket is the renal sinus, and the membranous glove that occupies the space is the renal pelvis.
4. Locate these structures in figure 44.2. The renal pelvis is connected to the ureter at the medial side of the kidney.

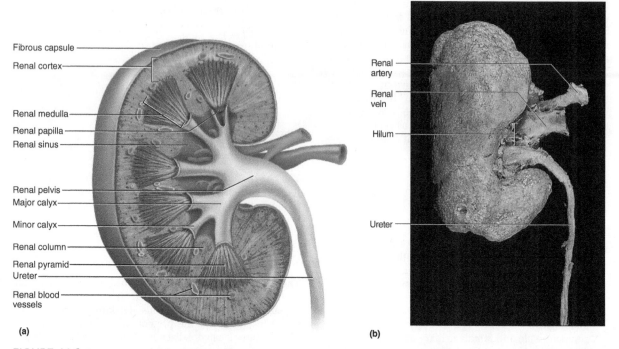

Fibrous capsule
Renal cortex

Renal medulla
Renal papilla
Renal sinus

Renal pelvis
Major calyx

Minor calyx

Renal column

Renal pyramid
Ureter

Renal blood
vessels

(a)

Renal
artery

Renal
vein

Hilum

Ureter

(b)

FIGURE 44.2 **Gross Anatomy of the Kidney, Entire and Coronal Section** (a) Diagram of coronal section of the kidney and details of renal pyramid; (b) photograph of entire kidney; (c) coronal section.

Blood Flow Through the Kidney

The kidney filters material from the blood and returns important material such as water, glucose, and sodium back to the blood. It is not a perfect system as some urea is also returned to the cardiovascular system. There is an arterial system that takes blood to the cortex of the kidney and several capillary beds, which is somewhat unusual compared to other organs. The venous system returns blood to the inferior vena cava.

Examine models or charts in lab and look at the vascular system in figure 44.3. The arterial system begins with the **renal artery,** which exits the **abdominal aorta** and enters the kidney. The arterial system branches extensively throughout the kidney. The first branches are the **segmental arteries,** which take blood from the renal artery. The segmental arteries are found inside the renal sinus. The kidney is divided into lobes, and there are **interlobar arteries** which take blood from the segmental arteries and pass through the renal columns.

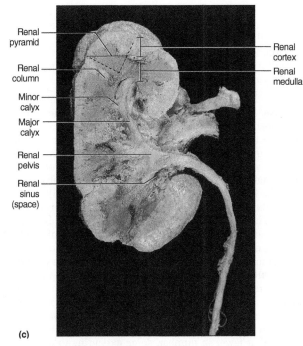

(c)

FIGURE 44.2 *Continued*

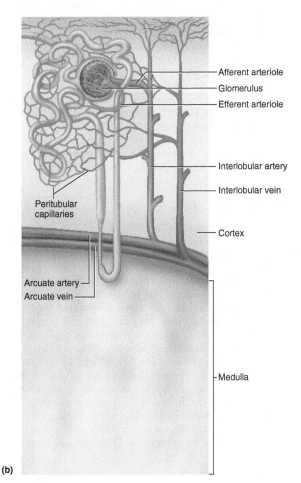

(b)

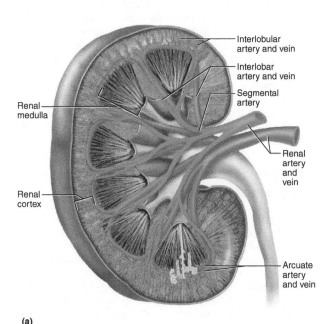

(a)

FIGURE 44.3 **Blood Flow Through the Kidney** (a) Major arteries and veins of the kidney; (b) diagram of blood flow.

The interlobar arteries are relatively large and make a sharp bend, becoming the **arcuate arteries.** The arcuate arteries form arcs between the cortex and the medulla, and they obtain their name from these arcs. Branching from the arcuate arteries are the **interlobular arteries** that move into the cortex of the kidney. The names *interlobar* and *interlobular* can be confusing at first, but the interlobar arteries are found in the medulla and are larger and the interlobular arteries are found in the cortex and are smaller.

In the cortex of the kidney, the interlobular arteries branch and form the **afferent arterioles,** which take blood to the **glomerulus,** a cluster of capillaries where filtration occurs. Blood then travels through the **efferent arterioles** and then to the **peritubular capillaries,** where reabsorption and secretion take place. In regions of the cortex near the medulla there are other vessels that branch from the efferent arteriole. These are the **vasa recta.** They represent only a small number of capillaries in the kidney, but they are important in producing a concentrated urine by reabsorption and secretion. The vasa recta are found in association with special nephrons called **juxtamedullary nephrons.**

Thus there are three capillary beds in the kidney, the **glomeruli** (plural of *glomerulus*), the peritubular capillaries, and the vasa recta. The blood flow in the kidney forms a **portal system,** which is defined as a group of blood vessels in which blood flows from one capillary bed (the glomerulus) to another capillary bed (the peritubular capillaries or vasa recta) with an arteriole or venule between them prior to returning to the heart.

The return flow to the heart occurs as blood returns via the **interlobular veins,** to the **arcuate veins,** to the **interlobar veins,** and to the **renal vein,** which leads to the inferior vena cava.

Ultrastructure of the Kidney

1. Before you examine the sections of kidney under the microscope, first become familiar with the structure of the **nephron.** Examine models and charts in the laboratory and compare them to figure 44.4.
2. Locate the **glomerular capsule (Bowman's capsule),** the **proximal convoluted tubule,** the **nephron loop (loop of Henle),** and the **distal convoluted tubule.** The glomerulus along with the glomerular capsule are known as the **renal corpuscle.** The nephron consists of the renal corpuscle, proximal convoluted tubule, nephron loop, and distal convoluted tubule. Blood travels to the nephron via the afferent arteriole. When the blood reaches the glomerulus (a cluster of capillaries in the renal cortex) the plasma is filtered by blood pressure forcing fluid across the capillary membranes. Blood pressure is the driving force for renal filtration, and this

pressure is opposed by hydrostatic pressure in the Bowman's capsule space outside of the glomerular capillaries and the osmotic pressure that occurs due to the proteins left in the blood plasma. This filtered fluid, present in the nephron, is called **filtrate.**

As the filtrate flows through the nephron, water, glucose, and many electrolytes are returned to the blood. The urea is concentrated as it passes through the nephron and the **collecting duct,** a tube that receives the fluid from the nephrons. The amount of reabsorption in the kidney varies with the material that flows through it. In normal conditions, glucose is completely reabsorbed into the blood. About 99% of the water in the filtrate is reabsorbed. Only 50% of the urea is excreted into the urine. The remainder of the urea returns to the blood and is filtered again. Urea is concentrated in the collecting duct, and some of it diffuses into the medulla, increasing the osmolarity in the medulla. This increases the flow of water out of the nephron, thus concentrating the urine.

There are two types of nephrons in the kidney. The majority of the nephrons are found in the cortex of the kidney and are thus called **cortical nephrons.** Those found in the medulla are called **juxtamedullary nephrons** and are far fewer in number, some extending to near the tip of the renal pyramids.

In summary, urine is produced from filtered blood. Some of the liquid portion of blood flows from the glomerulus into the nephron. Materials valuable to the body, such as glucose and other solutes, are reabsorbed by the nephron and return to the cardiovascular system by the peritubular capillaries. The main metabolic by-product, urea, is removed from the kidney and passes as urine from the collecting ducts to the minor calyces. The volume of urine and some of the constituents found in urine are controlled by hormones such as aldosterone and antidiuretic hormone (ADH). Aldosterone increases the reabsorption of sodium and reduces water volume. Antidiuretic hormone causes the distal convoluted tubules to reabsorb water, also decreasing the urine output.

Microscopic Examination of the Kidney

1. Examine a kidney slide under low power. You should see the cortex of the kidney, which has a number of round structures scattered throughout. These are the **glomeruli,** and they are composed of capillary tufts. The medullary region of the kidney slide has open, parallel spaces called **collecting ducts.** Compare the slide to figure 44.5a.
2. Examine the slide under higher magnification and locate the glomerulus and the **glomerular capsule.** The capsule is composed of simple squamous epithelium and specialized cells called podocytes.

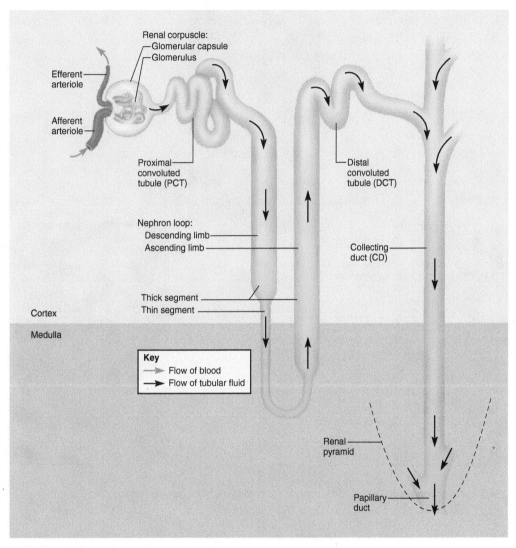

FIGURE 44.4 **Nephron**

3. Examine the outer edge of the capsule around the glomerulus. If you move the slide around in the cortex, you should find the proximal convoluted tubules with the **brush border** or microvilli on the inner edge of the tubule. The inner surface of the tubule appears fuzzy. The microvilli increase the surface area of the proximal convoluted tubule.

The distal convoluted tubules do not have brush borders; therefore, the inner surface of a tubule does not appear fuzzy. The cells of the distal convoluted tubules generally have darker nuclei and relatively clear cytoplasm when compared to the cells of the proximal convoluted tubules, as seen in figure 44.5b.

4. Examine the medulla of the kidney under high magnification and locate the thin-walled nephron loop and the larger-diameter collecting ducts, as seen in figure 44.5c.

Dissection of the Sheep Kidney

1. Place a sheep kidney on a dissection tray and dissection equipment on your table. Examine the outer **capsule** of the kidney. You may see some tubes coming from a dent in the kidney. The dent is the **hilum,** and the tubes are the **renal artery, renal vein,** and **ureter.** The renal artery is smaller

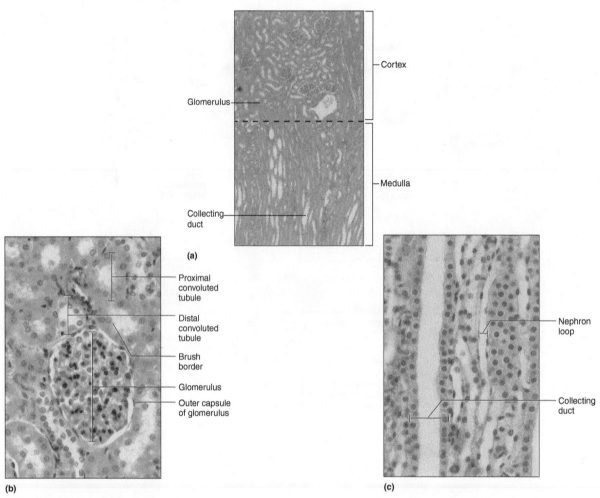

FIGURE 44.5 **Photomicrographs of a Kidney** (a) Overview (40×); (b) cortex (400×); (c) medulla (400×).

in diameter and has a thicker wall than the renal vein. The ureter has an expanded portion near the hilum.

2. Make an incision in the sheep kidney a little off center in the coronal plane (see figure 44.6). This section allows you to better see the interior structures of the kidney.

3. Locate the **renal cortex,** the outer layer of the kidney. You should also locate the **renal medulla,** which has triangular regions known as the **renal pyramids.** At the tip of each pyramid is a **papilla.** Urine from the papillae drips into the **minor calyx.** Many minor calyces lead to a **major calyx.** The **major calyces** take fluid to the **renal pelvis.**

4. Lift the renal pelvis somewhat to pull it away from the **renal sinus.** The sinus is the space in the kidney, which may be filled with adipose tissue. You should also examine the exit of the renal pelvis as it becomes the **ureter.**

5. When you are finished with the dissection, place the material in the proper waste container provided by your instructor.

Ureters

The ureters are long, thin tubes that conduct urine from the kidneys to the urinary bladder. The ureters have **transitional epithelium** as an inner lining and smooth muscle in their outer wall. Urine is expressed by peristalsis from the kidney to the urinary bladder. Examine the models in the lab and compare them to figures 44.1 and 44.6.

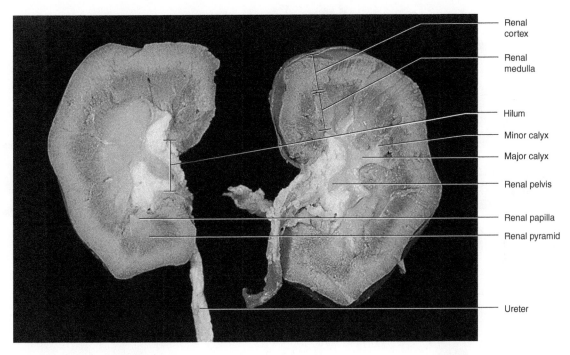

FIGURE 44.6 **Dissection of a Sheep Kidney**

Urinary Bladder

The **urinary bladder** is located anterior to the parietal peritoneum and is thus described as being **anteperitoneal.** Locate the urinary bladder in a torso model in lab. It is found just posterior to the symphysis pubis. On the posterior wall of the urinary bladder is a triangular region known as the **trigone.** The trigone is defined by the superior entrances of the ureters and the inferior exit of the urethra. Transitional epithelium lines the inner surface of the bladder, while layers of smooth muscle known as **detrusor muscles** are found in the wall of the bladder. Compare models in lab to figure 44.7.

Histology of the Bladder

Transitional epithelium has a special role in the urinary bladder. This epithelium can withstand a significant amount of stretching (distention) when the bladder fills with urine.

1. Examine a slide of transitional epithelium under the microscope and compare it to figure 44.8. Transitional epithelium is also discussed and illustrated in Laboratory Exercise 6.

2. Look at the inner surface of the section for the epithelial layer. The cells are shaped somewhat like teardrops. Transitional epithelium can be distinguished from stratified squamous epithelium in that the cells of transitional epithelium from an empty bladder do not flatten at the surface of the tissue. Below the transitional epithelium is an underlying layer known as the **lamina propria.**

3. Examine the smooth muscle layers of the urinary bladder that make up the detrusor muscle.

Urethra

The terminal organ of the urinary system is the **urethra.** The urethra is approximately 3 to 4 cm long in females. It passes from the urinary bladder to the **external urethral orifice** located anterior to the vagina and posterior to the clitoris, as seen in figures 44.7b and 44.9b. In figure 44.9 you can also see the position of the urinary bladder in relationship to the symphysis pubis. The urethra is about 20 cm long in males (figures 44.7a and 44.9a). It begins at the urinary bladder and passes through the prostate gland as the **prostatic urethra.** It continues and passes through the body wall as the **membranous urethra,** then exits

572   **LABORATORY 44** Urinary System

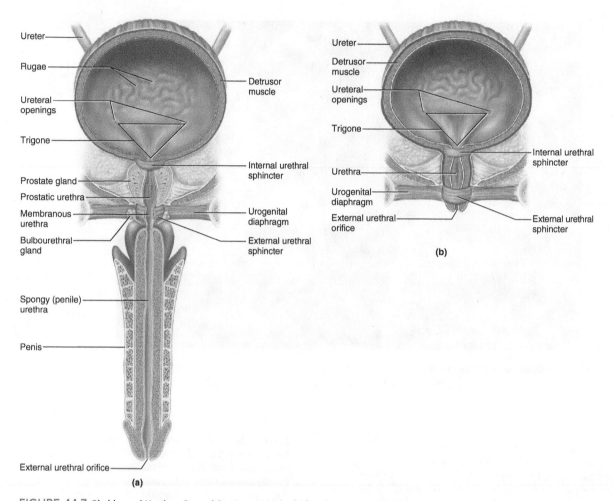

FIGURE 44.7 **Bladder and Urethra, Coronal Sections** (a) Male; (b) female.

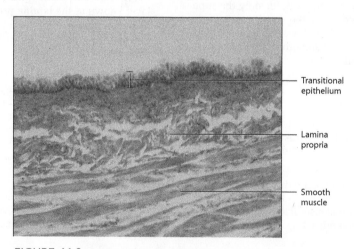

FIGURE 44.8 **Histology of the Bladder** (100×)

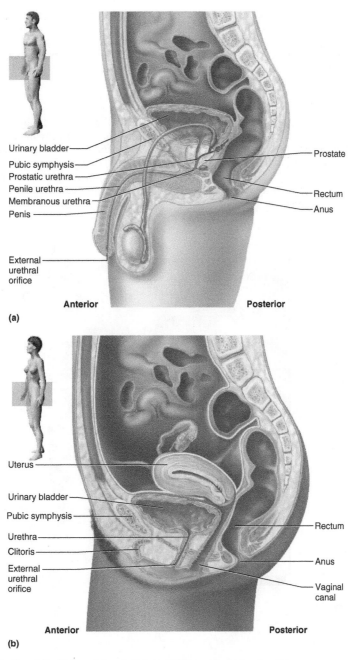

Urinary bladder

Pubic symphysis

Prostatic urethra

Penile urethra

Membranous urethra

Penis

External urethral orifice

Prostate

Rectum

Anus

Anterior   **Posterior**

(a)

Uterus

Urinary bladder

Pubic symphysis

Urethra

Clitoris

External urethral orifice

Rectum

Anus

Vaginal canal

Anterior   **Posterior**

(b)

FIGURE 44.9 **Midsagittal Section of the Male and Female Pelves** (a) Male pelvis; (b) female pelvis.

574   **LABORATORY 44**   Urinary System

through the penis to the external urethral orifice at the tip of the glans penis. This terminal portion of the urethra is known as the **penile, or spongy, urethra.** Urinary bladder infections are more common in females than in males (figures 44.7*a* and 44.9*a*) because of the difference in length in the urethra between males and females.

Cat Dissection

1. Open the abdominal region of the cat, if you have not done so already. The kidneys are on the dorsal body wall of the cat and are located dorsal to the parietal peritoneum.
2. Examine the kidneys and the structures that lead to and from the hilum of the kidney.

3. Find the renal veins that take blood from the kidney. The veins are larger in diameter than the renal arteries and they are attached to the posterior vena cava of the cat, which runs along the ventral, right side of the vertebral column.
4. Find the renal arteries that take blood from the aorta to the kidneys. The aorta lies to the left of the posterior vena cava.
5. Locate the ureters as they run posteriorly from the kidney to the urinary bladder.
6. Locate the urinary bladder. Do not dissect the urethra at this time. You can locate the urethra during the dissection of the reproductive structures in Exercises 46 and 47. You should compare your dissection to figure 44.10.

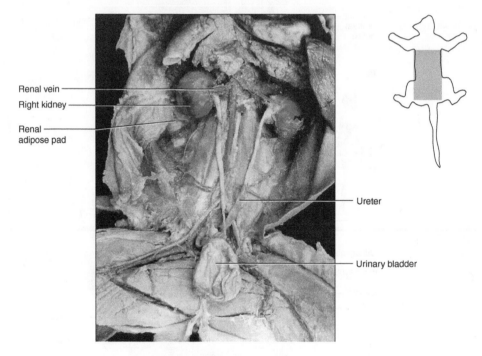

Renal vein

Right kidney

Renal adipose pad

Ureter

Urinary bladder

FIGURE 44.10 **Urinary System in the Cat**

EXERCISE

44

REVIEW SECTION ▪connect
|ANATOMY & PHYSIOLOGY

Urinary System

Name _____ Date _____

Lab Section _____ Time _____

Review Questions

Matching

Match the descriptions in the left column with the terms in the right column.

1. outermost part of the kidney
2. storage organ of the urinary system
3. takes blood from the kidney
4. separates the renal cortex from the medulla
5. receives urine from the renal papilla
6. leads directly to the renal pelvis

a. renal vein
b. major calyx
c. minor calyx
d. urinary bladder
e. fibrous capsule
f. arcuate arteries

Fill in

7. The _____ is found between the kidney and the urinary bladder.

8. The _____ is the terminal part of the nephron.

9. Filtration occurs at the _____ part of the nephron.

10. What is the outer region of the kidney called that contains glomeruli?

11. Describe the kidneys with regard to their position in relation to the parietal peritoneum.

12. What takes urine from the bladder to the exterior of the body?

13. What blood vessel takes blood to the kidney?

14. On the posterior bladder is a triangular region. What is it called?

15. Distal convoluted tubules flow directly into what structures?

16. What is a renal papilla?

17. Name the protective capsule that covers a kidney.

18. Blood in the glomerulus next flows to what arteriole?

19. Which shows the greatest anatomical difference between the sexes: ureters, urinary bladder, or urethra?

20. What histological feature distinguishes a proximal convoluted tubule from a distal convoluted tubule?

21. Name the parts of the nephron.

22. What type of cell lines the bladder?

23. Trace the flow of blood from the renal artery through the kidney to the renal vein.

24. What anatomical feature in females is responsible for the higher level of urinary tract infections in females?

25. Trace the path of filtrate and urine from the glomerulus to the external urethral opening.

26. Fill in the following illustration using the terms provided.

renal artery	renal vein	renal pelvis
minor calyx	major calyx	ureter
fibrous capsule	renal pyramid	renal cortex

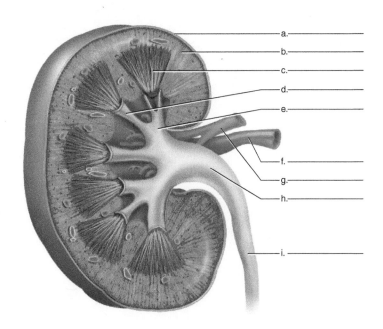

a. —————————

b. —————————

c. —————————

d. —————————

e. —————————

f. —————————

g. —————————

h. —————————

i. —————————

Notes